SPIRITUAL THERAPY

How the Physician, Psychiatrist and Minister Collaborate in Healing

SPIRITUAL

How the Physician, Psychiatrist and

Richard K. Young and Albert L. Meiburg

THERAPY

Minister Collaborate in Healing

Harper & Row, Publishers, New York

To David Vickers Young

and David McDougald Meiburg

CONTENTS

FOREWORD

The term "psychosomatic medicine," while of recent origin, describes an approach to medicine as old as the art of healing itself. Physicians have always known that the emotional life has something to do with illness but the structural concept introduced by Virchow led to the separation of illness from the psyche of man and considered disease only as a disorder of organs and cells. With this separation of diseases into many different ailments came the development of specialists to attend all of these distinct diseases. With the specialist came the introduction of instruments of precision, and the mechanization of medicine began. Medicine now contented itself with the study of the organism and the physiological mechanisms, impressed by biochemistry, X ray, electrocardiography, and other methods of investigation, but unimpressed and often holding in contempt the psychological background of the patient which was not considered as scientific as the results of the laboratory studies. It is not to be denied that remarkable developments occurred during this period of laboratory ascendancy but it must be admitted that the emotional side of illness was almost completely neglected. Every influence that bears upon man requires him to adapt himself to his circumstances, including both outward events and internal emotions. Profound changes manifested by alterations in body temperature, blood pressure, and blood sugar in the overreactive individual may produce physical changes in the organs. The vicious cycle then becomes completed and the psychosomatic illness becomes a somato-psychic illness, since few rational individuals can be physically ill without being emotionally upset as a result. A most graphic analysis of the problem was presented by Dr. A. J. Sullivan when he said: "Modern man is trying to find God in himself. Science with its great power has promised man independence from God. Our present world is seemingly eager to accept science as a way of salvation, but science is not a religion, not even medical science. Yet it is toward medicine that the sick and failing spirit turns. It would seem that science having unwittingly unfrocked the clergy has as unwittingly ordained the physician. We do not wish to argue that this should or should not be, but we must recognize that it has become a measurable trend."

It is not possible except in rare instances for the busy physician to minister to his patient's organic as well as his emotional and spiritual needs. Under such circumstances the medically oriented and trained clergyman is assuming his right and proper place as a member of the healing team. As a consultant for the sick and failing spirit he performs a function as necessary and valuable as that of other specialists called upon to add to a patient's understanding and comfort. To those of us to whom this valuable service is constantly available the art and practice of medicine has been made infinitely more effective and rewarding.

DAVID CAYER, M.D.
Professor of Internal Medicine
Bowman Gray School of Medicine
of Wake Forest College

PREFACE

An encouraging sign in this anxious culture is the renewal of the church's interest in the art of healing. Recent advances in the sciences of man are emphasizing the unity of his nature—mental, physical, and spiritual—so that whatever affects the part affects the whole. The church and medical science are moving in the right direction today in attempting to combine the best information gleaned from the disciplines of science with the health-giving resources of the Christian religion.

The pastor, like the physician, must ask the same basic questions if he is to make a specific rather than a general application of religion to the needs of a particular patient: "What kind of person am I dealing with? What has happened to this individual? How is he responding to his life situation? What are his specific religious needs at this time?"

In the course of a clinical training program we have consistently required our students to read relevant material on the emotional and spiritual dimensions of illness as found in medical literature. While this information has been helpful, at the same time it has required the student to face the problem of having to appropriate insights from another discipline. An example of this difficulty is the question often asked by a theological student at the end of a doctor's lecture, "What can the minister do to help in this situation?" Invariably the doctor appears puzzled, and rightly so, because he does not customarily approach the patient from a theological perspective.

Hence this book is an attempt to appropriate knowledge from medical disciplines relevant to the minister, and to illustrate how pastoral care can more effectively be given in the light of this information. No claim is made for originality or comprehensiveness in the presentation of medical information, although a serious effort has been made toward accuracy. This work is conceived as an adjunct to Young's earlier work, *The Pastor's Hospital Ministry*,[1] which dealt with the elementary principles of hospital visitation.

Case material appearing in this book is drawn from the accumulated records of the Department of Pastoral Care. The department holds a weekly staff conference at which the chaplain-intern reviews his total pastoral ministry to one patient. At this conference the physician who attended the patient is present to summarize the medical diagnosis and treatment. This material could not have been written without the generosity of the patients who allowed the chaplain access to the inner recesses of their souls. Many of these individuals told the minister to tell their experiences anywhere, to "shout it from the housetops," if it might help any other person to find a more abundant way of life. (For obvious reasons the patient's identity is completely disguised.)

This book has been written with the needs and interests of several groups of readers in mind. In the first place, it is intended for theological students in pastoral care training programs in seminaries and hospitals. References for additional reading are provided at the end of each chapter. It is hoped that the working pastor for whom the spiritual care of the sick is a daily responsibility will also find help through these pages. And finally, there is a growing interest among lay people in the relationship of their religious faith to their mental and physical well-being. We hope that the discussion of the various illnesses may lead the general reader to a better understanding of the person suffering from the illness, and in addition show how his minister may be able to help him find a more vigorous emotional and spiritual health.

It is impossible to acknowledge adequately the many contribu-

[1] Nashville: Broadman Press, 1954.

tions that have been made to this effort. Undoubtedly our philosophy reflects the thought of Sigmund Freud, Harry Stack Sullivan, and many other proponents of depth psychology. Likewise we are indebted to the major authorities in the rapidly growing field of pastoral care. This book, however, is not an effort to bring together all that has been written on the care of the sick. We have deliberately sought to write from our own case records and experience. We hope this limited work will contribute in some measure to the total body of literature in the field.

Physicians with whom we work have been more than gracious in reading the material for medical accuracy and making cogent suggestions. Specific acknowledgements to physicians are made within the chapters.

Special mention should be made of the assistance given by chaplain-interns serving in the department while this material was being prepared: Robert Barefield, William Carnes, Dwight Cumbee, Howard Durham, William Eastman, Dan Fielder, John Galloway, James Hall, James L. Harford, Eugene Johnson, Harry McCall, Harry Menzies, Robert Muhler, Lewis Myers, Jack Payne, Charles Phipps, Charles Smith, Truman Smith, Emory Young, and Herbert Zerof.

Our colleagues on the permanent staff of the department have offered valuable suggestions and clinical insights. Their encouraging interest and effectiveness in demonstrating and teaching pastoral care have been an unfailing support: Chaplains Everett Barnard, George Colgin, Robert Gunter, and Benjamin Patrick. The competent help of our receptionist and secretaries, Mrs. Mozelle Handy, Mrs. Frances Harvey, and Mrs. Isabel Jacobsen, has lightened the tedium of preparation.

Finally, we wish to offer a special word of gratitude to Dr. Clarence W. Hall, Senior Editor of *The Reader's Digest,* for his gracious Introduction. On several visits to our hospital to gather information about our work he refused to put up with generalizations and thereby helped us to be more specific than we would have been otherwise.

A clarification of authorship is in order here. The basic themes and philosophy have been maturing for fourteen years in Young's clinical experience in a medical center. Through the farsightedness of the governing body of the hospital it was possible to provide a research associate to the School of Pastoral Care. In this capacity, Meiburg is responsible for the collection of the relevant medical information on the illnesses. In the actual writing each has served as a sounding board to the other in the testing and clarification of ideas. The wording of no single sentence can be claimed exclusively by either.

If this book does nothing else we hope it will encourage minister-doctor co-operation. If it can serve in some way to push forward the effort to release more of religion's creative and curative powers in the lives of distressed people, then our efforts will be more than amply repaid.

RICHARD K. YOUNG
ALBERT L. MEIBURG

INTRODUCTION

SPIRITUAL THERAPY: MODERN MEDICINE'S NEWEST ALLY *

by

CLARENCE W. HALL

Senior Editor, *The Reader's Digest*

The young mother in the emergency ward at Winston-Salem's North Carolina Baptist Hospital was sinking rapidly. Her baby had been killed in the auto smashup, but her own injuries did not seem serious enough to be fatal. After the surgeon had done all he could, he called in a psychiatrist. "There's no medical reason why she shouldn't recover," he said. "But she wants to die—and she will, unless her attitude is changed."

The psychiatrist's careful analysis uncovered the root of the woman's problem: the baby killed had been born as the result of an extramarital affair. She had been able to live with her secret as long as the child was alive, but now nothing the psychiatrist said could shake her guilt-ridden interpretation of the accident's meaning. "I've got to die," she kept repeating. "It's God's punishment for my sin. I deserve it."

* Condensed from an article in *The Reader's Digest*, September 1959, and reprinted by permission.

15

The psychiatrist summoned the chaplain. "This case calls for theological answers I haven't got," he said.

On several occasions the chaplain visited the patient, saying little, allowing her to express her remorse fully. When she was exhausted, he said quietly, "You say you must die. But isn't killing yourself—and that's what you're doing—just taking the easy way out? The selfish way? Your death will only bring what you feel is your judgment upon your fine husband and your other child. Do you think that's fair?"

During a long silence he let this sink in, then said softly, "Wouldn't you like to use this tragedy to redeem your marriage and your life?"

Reassured and shown an avenue of hope, the woman cried, "Oh, I would, I would!"

And she did. Once she had found a new purpose in living, her wounds healed rapidly. She has been an exemplary wife and mother ever since.

The minister who effected this spiritual therapy was a member of the staff recruited and trained by the Rev. Richard K. Young, director of the School of Pastoral Care at North Carolina Baptist. Young is a firm believer in the therapeutic value of practically applied religion. And his highly successful pioneering in this field has led to the idea of a hospital "healing team" in which doctor, psychiatrist, and clergyman pool their disparate talents to mount a co-ordinated assault on disease.

One of the first things Young discovered was that "an individual rarely states the real nature of his problem in a first encounter." The deception is not intentional. Filled with fear, anxiety, guilt, or humiliation, our subconscious minds provide all kinds of ingenious excuses for acting as we do.

"The symptom itself is so pressing, its side effects so devastating," says Young, "that it blocks out the condition that caused it. Even if patients have insight into the real problem, they don't know how to handle it. Slowly, gradually, they must be led to see the real problem and draw upon resources, both inside and outside themselves, to lick it."

There was, for example, the man whose *stated* problem, after a seeming heart attack, was: "I'm scared to death to drive my car. Yet I must; I'm a traveling salesman." Counseling revealed that his *real* problem was a fear of having to violate his conscience by drinking with customers who expected liquid entertainment. When he accepted the necessity of boldly standing up for his beliefs, the problem faded; he won the respect of his customers, became one of the most successful salesmen in his large firm.

Also, there was the patient whose chest pains and heart palpitation were, he was sure, caused by "business tensions." A medical checkup showed no heart disorder. Only, when, in talking with Dick Young, he mentioned his hostility to in-laws who lived next door and "hem me in and criticize me all the time," did he come to see that his tensions were symptoms! the real trouble was his unwillingness to face his own personality defects.

"When this man got his hoarded resentments out in the open, he began to see why his in-laws reacted to him as they did. He went home to establish a more mature relationship with them—and his cardiac symptoms never reappeared. Best of all, he became an individual in his own right."

As Young pioneered the techniques of getting beyond symptoms to root troubles, he came to see that three factors were of paramount importance. These were "relating," "accepting," and "listening." "Relating" required that the counselor convince the patient that he was sharing his experience with someone who understood and cared, who perhaps could see his situation more objectively than he himself could, and who wanted, more than anything else in the world, to help. "Accepting" demanded that the counselor show no evidence of moral disapproval no matter how distasteful the patient's revelations. "Listening" ("the heart of all effective counseling," Young says) had to be "active, reassuring, interpretative."

The most delicate part of the counseling process, Young found, came when the story was all out, the catharsis complete. Having fully unburdened themselves—which might take many hours, or even weeks—patients tended to feel an overwhelming sense of relief.

It was sometimes difficult to convince them that this was not a cure, but merely the first step back to health.

To a woman who came with a marriage problem and, after what seemed like full ventilation of her disrupted home situation, exclaimed with a sigh, "Oh, I feel so relieved; now I'm cured!" Dick Young said gently, "Tell me, *what are you cured of?*" The woman stammered, "Why, as I've talked, I've resolved not to nag my husband any longer, but just accept him and his failings."

Young said, "Is that all? Then we need to talk some more." Slowly she began to see that the actions of her husband, his "failings," were largely reactions against her own determination to make him over, her unwillingness to accept him as a person. "When she saw *that,* and was ready to begin work on herself, she *was* cured. And so, in time, was her sick marriage."

Giving a patient insight into his real problem was sometimes enough. Often it wasn't. Some patients had to be jolted into action by what Dick Young calls his "shock therapy." To a man whose problem was a secret affair with his secretary, but who dallied over breaking it off, he said tartly, "You're wasting my time. You know what you must do. Make a decision one way or another, and stick with it." The man did, and both his health and his marriage were saved.

He was no less blunt with a brawny troublemaker who, facing serious surgery, was obviously covering up his fears by profane bluster that upset nurses and other patients—and hoisted his own temperature to hazardous levels. To him Dick Young said pointedly, "Why do you think it's necessary to throw your weight around? You're just scared, and you know it." Surprised, the big man discarded his bluster. Tears came into his eyes. "You're right, chaplain. Will you pray for me while I'm on the operating table?" Young promised; the man was on the table for five hours, but came through well. "Today," Young says, "he is one of my best friends."

The line of demarcation between psychiatry and spiritual counseling is fixed in neither theory nor practice. "We meet in the middle of the individual's emotions," Young defines it tersely. But this unmarked boundary has never affected his warm co-operation with the hospital psychiatric staff. When he found himself baffled by a patient's symptoms, Young would drop into the office of Dr. Angus Randolph, then resident psychiatrist, describe the case and conclude frankly, "I can't make any sense of it at all. Do you see a pattern here?"

The close working relationship that developed soon proved its value to both men. The psychiatric clinic was swamped with a huge case load. Young's presence enabled its staff to weed out those who were more in need of a trained minister's counseling than of full-dress psychiatric treatment, and thereby concentrate on the most serious cases. Young in turn would sometimes uncover deep-seated psychopathic tendencies in the course of routine marriage counseling; by referring the victims immediately to the psychiatric staff he materially increased their chances of recovery.

In 1947, following the plan he'd had in mind from the beginning, Young decided that it was time to pass along to others what he had learned, and launched his now famous School of Pastoral Care. The hospital backed the project with enthusiasm and, from a first pilot class of eight carefully selected students, enrollment has steadily increased year by year.

To reach the largest possible number of ministers, training is now provided at several different levels. Ten internships of a year's duration are offered annually, five of them salaried and limited to Baptists only, the other five open to all denominations. Trainees in this program rank with the hospital's medical and surgical interns, and each year two of them are given a further year of residency training. Recurrent six-week courses for pastors are also offered from September through May, and eight-week summer courses for seminary students. Some 500 ministers thus clinically trained by Young are now applying their insights in 30 states and 14 foreign countries, including Nigeria, Thailand, Japan, India, and New Zealand.

Dick Young is deeply convinced that pastoral care of the sick is so delicate an art that no seminary should graduate ministers without it. To divinity students at Southeastern Baptist Theological Seminary, where he is an associate professor of pastoral theology, he says, "In most states law does not permit a medical doctor to go directly from the classroom to practice medicine; he must have a year of supervised clinical experience. How much more should this principle apply to the training of physicians of the soul!"

All classes are limited to ten persons, and lectures are kept to a minimum. "Skill in intensive counseling does not come by reading a book or hearing a lecture," Dick Young says. "It comes by exposing yourself to the hurt of humanity." His staff and students made 70,000 such "exposures" last year alone. Brought face to face with people in their most agonized moments, seminarians find the experience both humbling and spiritually challenging. Pastors find it revitalizing, if not revolutionary, to their ministry. "It makes them not only better persons," Young said, "but also better theologians."

He tells of one seminary graduate, a Ph.D. from an Ivy League university, who swept grandly into the school and annoyed everyone with his stance of superiority. "He'd majored in psychology, knew psychiatry's jargon, could quote from every authority on pastoral counseling—yet had never met a really troubled person face to face." After putting up patiently with the young man's lofty theological theory, laced with Freudian lingo, Young said quietly, "Go up to Floor 3, Room 7. There you'll find Mrs. Brown. She has a problem." In an hour the know-it-all was back. Humbled, wearing a sheepish grin, he said, "I know why you sent me up there. How *does* one help a person like that?"

Young himself never uses the complex technical language of psychiatry, although he knows it well. "I'm convinced you don't really understand something," he says, "unless you can talk with *anybody* about it." And he tells his students, "You're being trained to become not junior-league psychiatrists, but ministers of the grace of God, *practical* theologians. No pat answers or canned solutions will do for people whose problems are as personal as their thumbprints."

In his view, a simple prayer and an exhortation to read the Bible and think positively may be a superficial panacea but seldom a cure. When a young pastor taking part-time clinical training jubilantly reported that he had healed a broken marriage, Young asked how he'd done it. "Oh, I got the pair down on their knees together, prayed with them, then had them kiss and make up." Next week when the student returned, Young asked, "How are your reunited couple making out?" Crestfallen, the young pastor replied, "They're not. They separated that same day, never even spent the night together."

Pastoral care that is mostly exhortation, says Young, is "placing a truth down over a trouble, not rooting it out; sooner or later the emotional problem will blow the lid off."

Sending his students into the rooms and wards, he tells them, "If you know anything about man's heartbreak and God's love, here's the place to apply that understanding. Up on those floors you won't hear what the poets call the music of the spheres. You'll hear what Wordsworth called the 'still, sad music of humanity.' Absorb it—until it breaks your heart!"

To test their "absorbing" ability he requires "verbatims"—fully written reports of interviews with patients. Brought to seminars, these verbatims are studied by the staff, discussed in class, subjected to piercing analysis. To measure growth in "receptive and reflective" listening, Young submits each student to a scientific "listening test" at the start and conclusion of his course.

"What you learn here," Young tells his trainees, "will be as useful in a parish as in the chaplaincy. Every church, every community, is full of people with problems. Clinical training will make you better ministers—wherever you are called to serve."

Dealing with guilt feelings—the sense of having sinned against oneself, against some other person, against God—is perhaps the number-one problem in Young's School of Pastoral Care.

Nowhere is modern psychiatry undergoing so sharp a revision of thought as in its approach to these morbid symptoms. The theory used to be: dredge up your guilt feelings, talk about them, look at them in the light of day—and they'll go away. "The trouble," says one prominent psychoanalyst, "was that for many they didn't go away. I discovered that it takes more than just uncovering guilt as the psychogenic factor in illness; there must be an assurance of forgiveness. For such patients I now engage the help of a minister."

Before this attitude became widespread, doctors often resented Young's delving into guilt feelings. Anxious to keep their patients relaxed, their blood pressure down, they feared anything that would make a patient even temporarily more tense. To one such, Young said bluntly, "The medical profession must learn that a chaplain's role itself arouses guilt. He doesn't have to say a word; his very presence does it. A patient must often get worse emotionally before he can get better physically and spiritually. Peace of mind is no more possible to a man harboring real guilt than is bodily health to a man with a hidden cancer. I'd no sooner try to create spiritual tranquillity in the admittedly guilty—even for so excellent a reason as keeping his blood pressure down—than you would slap a Band-Aid on a festering boil!"

A case in point was that of Tom Arnold,* a puzzler to the whole gastroenterology section of the hospital. For over a year the forty-three-year-old businessman had been treated for repeated severe relapses of ulcerative colitis. Now Tom was back with his most acute attack—one that might easily prove fatal.

Dick Young was called in. "Something's eating this man," said the gastrointestinal specialist, "that neither the psychiatrist nor I have been able to discover. He has admitted mental and emotional stress over a divorce two years ago, plus various business worries. And he's had the best help psychiatry can give in handling such anxieties. But I suspect we've both been treating symptoms. Maybe you can uncover the real cause."

For hours Young sat by Tom's bedside, skillfully leading him to talk about his problems. Finally Tom blurted, "There's something else I haven't told you; I've got to get it off my chest." And out came the details of an affair he was having with a married woman. "Just yesterday," he said, "her husband found out. Last night I got this attack. There must be some connection. What can I do?"

The chaplain replied, "You've diagnosed your own case; you can write your own prescription. Isn't it that you must break off this affair, confess, and ask forgiveness of the two people you've

* Real names of patients herein are changed, for obvious reasons.

wronged and of the God whose laws you've violated? You can be well only when you're ready to take that medicine. Are you?"

Tom Arnold was ready—and did. In the five years since, he has had no recurrence of colitis.

Guilt feelings take many forms, produce many complications. Even when no actual wrong has been done, merely dallying with the temptation to transgress our own moral standards can induce degenerative symptoms.

Such was the curious case of Everett Barton, brought in with a paralyzed right arm. A neurologist could find nothing physically wrong. His motor responses, even in the affected member, were perfect.

The doctor said, "You have what we call functional paralysis. Will you see one of our psychiatrists?"

Barton flared. "Of course not. I'm not crazy. It's my arm. You're a specialist—cure it!"

The neurologist shrugged. "We'll try." Back in his office he called the School of Pastoral Care. Within the hour Dick Young casually stopped at Barton's bedside, introduced himself. "Glad to see you, Chaplain," said Barton. "I'm pretty active in church myself; financial secretary. Easy job for me, though; I'm an accountant by trade."

Young deftly led the conversation around to the difficulties of relating one's Christian faith to the realistic demands of secular work. Barton responded, "Don't I know it! I've been with one firm for twenty years. Just the other day my employer asked me to manipulate the firm's accounts—for income-tax purposes. When I objected, he hinted that he could get another bookkeeper. But this arm trouble developed before I could get started."

"Think there's any connection?" Young asked.

"How could there be?" Barton demanded.

Young explained: "A man's conscience is a powerful thing; may it not be that yours resolved this moral problem for you by making it physically impossible to obey your employer?"

Barton nodded thoughtfully. "But what can I do?" he asked. "I'm getting along in years, and jobs aren't plentiful."

"We all have to make our own decisions," Young replied. "But I have a notion that if you stick with your conscience your paralysis will disappear."

The next day Barton went home, explained to his employer why he couldn't be a party to dishonesty—and almost immediately regained the use of his arm. Instead of being fired, he got a raise. Said his employer, "That conscience of yours taught us both a lesson!"

In Dick Young's view, the Bible is the perfect casebook in this area of psychotherapy. God is described as one "who forgiveth all thine iniquities and healeth all thy diseases." Says Young, "Note the sequence there! Christ invariably addressed his prescription for healing to the spiritual, first. To the palsied man asking only for physical help, he said, 'Son, thy *sins* be forgiven thee'—and the palsy disappeared. Knowing that a healed body with a sin-guilty soul would soon relapse, he said to the paralytic healed at the Bethesda pool, 'Sin no more, lest a worse thing come unto thee.'

"It's as true today as it was when that Book was written: the most powerful force in the universe is Christian love."

Just as the sound application of religious insights can be used to cure the sick, so religious misconceptions and distortions can often contribute to illness. The view of God as vengeful, vindictive, spying on human frailty in order to punish us—an image sometimes invoked by parents in an unthinking effort to "discipline" their children—underlies a common pattern of neurotic guilt feelings. When any injury or illness strikes, victims of such garbled teachings quickly conclude, "It's God's punishment for something I've done!"

Closely allied is the morbid fear of having committed an "unpardonable sin." Although, according to Young, "nine out of ten people who use this phrase can't define what they mean by it to save their lives," the obsession can be emotionally devastating. Gripped by an overwhelming sense of despair, such patients frequently adopt what psychologists call a "death wish." Restoring their will to live, a task for which the clerical members of the healing team are uniquely suited, can often mean the difference between life and death.

Says Dr. Eben Alexander, neurosurgeon and chief of professional services at the hospital, "Every doctor knows from bitter experience that when a patient says, 'Doctor, I'm going to die,' the chances are that, no matter how minor the procedure or how skillful the treatment, the patient *will* die." Except in emergency cases where delay would be fatal, Dr. Alexander refuses to operate until such a patient's outlook can be changed. "But," he says, "our chaplains can often achieve that change."

Sometimes the analysis of religious symptoms attendant upon physical illness can lead to the solution of otherwise baffling cases. Such was the problem of a woman admitted to the hospital with a crippling functional disorder which defied ordinary medical diagnosis. Interviewed by a chaplain, she confided in hopeless tones, "I've lost my relationship to God."

As the counselor carefully reviewed the history of her religious maladjustment, the signs of a closely related underlying problem gradually emerged. After her marriage, the woman had moved back to her father's farm with her husband. There they had become embroiled in a bitter dispute over crop management, and as a result she had not spoken to her father in over a year. As time passed, her depression over this alienation grew so intense that she became unable to pray. Convinced that she was isolated from God, she had fallen victim to the illness which brought her to the hospital. With these facts at their disposal, the chaplain and the psychiatric staff, working in conjunction, were able to restore the woman's sense of emotional and religious harmony, and as a result her physical symptoms rapidly ameliorated.

Of course, not all the problems the School of Pastoral Care deals with call for "theological answers." "We do not throw the Bible at everyone," says Young.

There are, for example, patients who, consciously or unconsciously, *use* their illnesses to escape from some intolerable situation, to secure affection not given them in health, to gain sympathy for their "martyrdom." Confounding medical wisdom by refusing to get well, such people make up a large proportion of the chronically ill who, according to medical surveys, consume from one half to three fourths of busy doctors' and nurses' time.

There was, for example, the young woman who was repeatedly brought to the hospital—each time with a different malady. "Every germ in the neighborhood seems to hit me," she reported. Dick Young discovered that she and her husband lived next door to her mother—a dominating, overprotective woman who, ever since her daughter's girlhood bout with rheumatic fever, had insisted on running her life. "Why am I such a weakling?" the girl wailed. Young replied, "Move to the other side of town." She did, more than three years ago—and hasn't been back to the hospital since.

The characteristic attitude of the martyr type—an exaggerated sense of "duty"—can often induce hypertension. Such was the case of a woman in her middle fifties, whose excessively high blood pressure, resisting all medication, puzzled cardiac specialists. Dick Young took over, gradually getting the patient to talk at length about her family. The story that came out: she had been the oldest child of a large family. When she was fourteen, her mother died, saying, "Dear, now you must take my place." For years she kept the promise, refusing to marry until all the others had homes of their own. Even after her own marriage she felt responsible, spending herself endlessly for those who no longer needed her.

At the end of the long recital, Young said, "Your family must be grateful to you for sacrificing your own interests to mother them through the years." The woman's glow of pleasure faded a little when he added, "But isn't it wonderful that they now are all happily able to care for themselves and you are free at last?" Then understanding swept over her face. "I'm *not* responsible any more, am I? How silly I've been! They probably would be happier if I quit interfering, wouldn't they?"

Says her doctor, "Almost immediately her blood pressure sank to nearly normal—and stayed there. Her whole life was altered. She's now leading an active, full existence—without the artificial burden she had refused to let go until Dick Young led her to see what she was doing to herself and the others."

Stories of similar healing achievements are legion. But Dick Young would be the last to claim that spiritual therapy invariably cures all persons of their ills. Or much less solves all the problems that caused them. Many take years to work out. The important thing is, he says, that we gain insight into our real trouble and identify our resources for handling it.

Many of his patients are like the woman with a difficult marital situation who, after weeks of intensive counseling, returned to say, her face radiant, "Things at home haven't changed much. But *I* have!"

Another particularly fruitful adjunct to the center's healing facilities is the "outpatient counseling service." This service enables the hospital to follow a patient into his home and community, where his troubles were bred in the first place.

The outpatient service handles over 4500 visits per year from men and women suffering kindred difficulties. Many come from more than 100 miles away for each session; almost half come from outside Winston-Salem.

In addition, "extended care" is supplied by the network of pastors (237 in North Carolina alone) who have taken clinical training under Young and who now give concentrated pastoral attention to ex-patients and their families. Hundreds of doctors, many trained at the Bowman Gray School of Medicine, stand ready to join with these pastors in applying to the healing-team approach to keeping discharged patients well.

The spread of the healing-team concept, particularly in the South, is almost as impressive as its practice at the Baptist medical center in Winston-Salem. Alumni of the School of Pastoral Care return to their parishes to promote doctor-minister get-togethers on a community-wide basis. As a result, throughout the Southeast you can hear hundreds of stories of successful co-operation. A prominent Southern doctor proudly told me, "Nowhere else in the country are so many ministers and doctors joining forces to conquer human ills. Men of the two professions—some of whom for years were scarcely on speaking terms—are realizing at last how closely allied their disciplines are." Speaking before the Texas Medical Association, its president, Dr. Milford O. Rouse, declared that "the most fundamental of all partnerships in medicine is with the ministry."

To Dick Young this modern alliance is new in practice but not in concept. "Almost two dozen centuries ago," he says with a wry grin creasing his lean face, "the author of the *Charmides* dialogue wrote that 'if the head and the body are to be well, you must begin by curing the soul; that is the first thing.' We're just catching up with Plato!"

Psychiatry, too, is moving gradually toward similar co-operation with religion. Sparked by a serious desire for mutual understanding of each other's disciplines, more than a dozen top-level meetings between clergymen of all faiths and psychiatrists of all schools were held during the past three years alone. "The greatest discovery of modern psychiatry is the soul," says one prominent psychiatrist, "not as just another name for the mind, but as an area in its own right, affecting both mind and body for good or ill."

Famed British psychiatrist Dr. J. A. Hadfield maintains, "As a student of psychotherapy who, as such, has no concern with theology, I am convinced that the Christian religion is one of the most potent influences we possess for producing that harmony and confidence of soul needed to bring health to a large proportion of nervous patients." After thirty years of experience Freud's great disciple Jung confessed that among all his patients over thirty-five "not one has been really healed who did not regain his religious outlook."

To supply the increasing demand for hospital chaplains, trained as "physicians of the soul," a number of groups are working furiously to stimulate interest in religious therapy as the "third dimension in healing." Such groups are co-operating under the National Advisory Council on Clinical Pastoral Education.

In accepting its new role in healing, says the Rev. George C. Anderson, founder of the National Academy of Religion and Mental Health, "religion may be on the verge of developments as revolutionary as the Protestant Reformation."

Dick Young summarizes the modern practice of comprehensive healing as follows:

The *physician* says, "Here is a body that is sick. I will address myself to that sickness, and with the latest drugs and surgical techniques I will make this body well."

The *psychiatrist* says, "Here is a mind with an anxiety that has made the patient physically and mentally ill. By analysis I will help him gain insight into his problem, and by drawing upon his own resources he can help heal himself."

The *minister* says, "Here is an immortal soul, whose sick body and disturbed mind have defeated him as a person. By giving him love and understanding, and by pointing him to resources outside himself, I will help him get beyond his body-mind disorders to their underlying cause: his sense of disharmony with himself, his fellows, and his God."

Together all members of the healing team say, "Here is a man who is body, mind, and soul. His whole health is the sum of the health of the three. Only by working together, each in his own specialty, can we heal the whole man."

Dick Young finds it intriguing that this modern move toward co-operation comes more enthusiastically from leaders in the medical field than from those in the religious. "In inviting clergymen to join physicians in their total approach to the total person," he says, "medical science is affording the church its greatest opportunity since Christ commanded His disciples to 'preach the gospel and heal the sick.'"

It strikes him as significant that not over a church door but over the entrance to one of America's greatest medical centers (Columbia-Presbyterian in New York City) is engraved the legend: *"For from the Most High cometh healing."*

ONE *Spiritual Therapy for the Heart Patient*

Heart disease today is our leading killer. In fact more than half of all Americans who died from illness in 1956 succumbed to diseases of the heart and blood vessels. Part of the dread connected with this illness results from the fact that it often strikes swiftly and without warning. For those who survive, no other disease, with the possible exception of mental illness, handicaps its victims for self-support so suddenly.

Some of the circumstances which influence pastoral care of the person who has experienced a heart attack can be seen in the following case. George Wood, a fifty-one-year-old insurance salesman, was apparently in good health until five o'clock on the evening of his admission to the hospital. While preparing to leave his office he developed a sudden sharp pain in his chest and was immediately hospitalized. His physician diagnosed his illness as coronary thrombosis. By 5:45 P.M. he was in his bed in an oxygen tent and described by his physician as being in a state of shock.

The chaplain talked with Mrs. Wood in the hall while the doctor was attending her husband. "This is a great shock to me," she said; "he has always been in such good health." She told the chaplain that her husband had complained of being tired the night be-

The authors wish to acknowledge their gratitude to Robert McMillan, M.D., Professor of Clinical Internal Medicine, Bowman Gray School of Medicine and Cardiologist at North Carolina Baptist Hospital, for contributing to this chapter and reading the whole for medical accuracy.

fore. "I guess he has worked too hard. He's married to his job," she explained. "When I left him a few minutes ago the last thing he said was, 'Be sure to call the boss and tell him about my condition!' He's a good man," she continued. "He won't complain and tell you how he really feels. I wonder if he realizes the seriousness of his condition. He told me he had a bad case of indigestion."

The chaplain assured her that he would remember both her and her husband in prayer. He did not attempt any ministry to Mr. Wood at this time.

On the next day when he called at the nursing station the chaplain learned that Mr. Wood was sleeping and was unable to be interviewed even by the resident physician for any length of time.

On the third day the chaplain found Mr. Wood out of the oxygen tent and feeling some better. He told the chaplain his sickness was like President Eisenhower's. "The president got all right," he said, "and I think I will too." Introducing his roommate, who was also convalescing from a heart attack, he said, "We are going to have a race to see who will be the first to get out of bed."

On the next visit Mr. Wood's bed was elevated and he was reading. In reply to "How are things going?" by the chaplain, he said, "Oh, I'm feeling fine. I could walk out the door and leave the hospital, but the doctor won't let me."

Since Mrs. Wood had commented earlier that her husband would not say how he really felt about things the chaplain was somewhat astonished with what followed in the conversation.

"My doctor had a long chat with me this morning. He said that there is no reason why I should be handicapped for the rest of my life. My attitude toward this illness, according to him, will have a great deal to do with determining my future. Of course I am going to have to drive around here in low gear for awhile, but he says I can live as long as I would have otherwise if I plan my life properly."

After a brief pause Mr. Wood added, "Chaplain, my wife and I have about decided that what has happened to me is a blessing in disguise."

"You mean that you have learned something from your illness?" asked the chaplain.

"Yes," Mr. Wood continued, "I have been a slave to my insurance business. Strange, isn't it, how sometimes the good Lord has to knock us down to teach us something?"

"You may have a point there, Mr. Wood," responded the chaplain. "Do you remember those words in the twenty-third Psalm where it says, *'He maketh me to lie down in green pastures'?*"

"Yes, and I think I understand the rest of the Psalm better now than I ever did before. Would you read it for me and have a prayer before you go?"

"Certainly," said the chaplain.

After reading the familiar lines of the Psalm, the chaplain offered a prayer of thanksgiving for the new insight that had come to Mr. Wood through his illness and asked God's blessing on him as he redirected his life in the light of his new experience. On subsequent visits until his discharge the chaplain found Mr. Wood maintaining the same healthy attitudes, except for occasional mild bouts of depression.

Since the pastoral care of heart patients is a recurring task of the minister, he should know something about the general characteristics of this illness.

The most prominent symptom associated with heart disease is probably that of pain. The pain may be sudden and fleeting as in angina pectoris or it may be drawn out over a period of days as sometimes occurs with the illness known medically as myocardial infarction. The latter type of pain is different from that experienced in any other kind of illness. It is overwhelming and tends to leave the patient in a state of despair. The sudden, excruciating pain creates fear in the patient that he is going to die. Even cancer does not pose the threat of immediate death as does a heart attack.

One will observe as many different emotional reactions to pain as there are people. These reactions may range all the way from overwhelming panic at the one extreme to stoical denial on the other. Patients with angina pectoris quite often deny the significance of their symptoms by word or behavior. In discussing their diagnosis they tend to avoid using the word "heart." You will notice that Mr. Wood circumvented the use of the word "heart" by saying, "I have the same thing Mr. Eisenhower had." In some cases cardiac patients refuse hospitalization or persist in excessive activity against medical advice.

Anxiety in the face of imminent death is a second prominent characteristic associated with the heart attack. Underlying concerns of the patient may be brought to the surface. Failure to achieve personal goals, an intolerable home situation, guilt, or unresolved grief are among the issues which the patient may desire to share with the pastor at this time. One cardiac patient in telling of his sense of loss in the death of his wife ten years before declared, "I just can't put my *heart* into my work."

The role of the emotions as causative factors in organic heart impairment has not been finally established, but the patient with a cardiac complaint needs alleviation of anxiety regardless of whether his symptoms are on an organic or functional basis. The anxious person with a healthy heart may be reassured by the physician and told to go back to work. Whereas an anxious person with a diseased heart when surrounded by precautions and told to rest may become an invalid. He is crippled more from fear of the heart disease than from the heart disease itself.

Fear can hinder normal recovery from a heart attack as seen in the case of a fifty-five-year-old man with acute coronary thrombosis. The patient refused to be hospitalized, and insisted that the doctor treat him at home. Furthermore, he viewed with disdain all the doctor's orders. He continued to smoke, chew tobacco, ate a full breakfast of country ham the next morning, and refused to stay in bed. When the physician called on him at home the patient asked, "Do I have what Fred Brown had?"

"Yes," replied the physician, not knowing that Fred Brown, a close friend of the patient, had dropped dead that morning.

The patient took to his bed and remained there for eight months after his heart attack. The physician reported, "He wouldn't even scratch his nose!" Finally the physician had to move him to the hospital to get him out of the bed.

At the hospital he would venture from his bed only with the help of the doctor and with each step would look at him as if to

say, "Is this my last one?" Two months were required for his rehabilitation. He returned to his work and became a leader in his
vocation; retiring from his company at his full salary, he died with
cancer of the bladder at seventy.[1]

Anxiety arising from the possibility of imminent death changes
during the convalescent period to discouragement and varying stages
of depression. It is possible for extreme anxiety, worry, and depression to precipitate further cardiac failure. For this reason pastoral
care in some instances could tip the balance between life and death.

We had a patient in our hospital who had been critically ill
with heart disease for two weeks. Because his blood pressure was excessively high, the doctor prescribed a sedative and under its effect
his blood pressure dropped to normal. This hinted at an emotional
overlay in his illness in addition to his heart condition. In talking
with the doctor the chaplain remembered that the patient had shown
some concern over how much his disability as a wage earner would
affect his future. The doctor then gave the patient an exercise toler-
ance test. The results of this test provided a basis for counseling
with him about the extent to which he could resume his former activities. The chaplain and the doctor working together helped the
patient to realize that he could slow down and still maintain his
job responsibilities without jeopardizing his dearly won hold on life.

In addition to the onslaught of pain and anxiety, a third major
problem faced by the heart patient is his loss of self-esteem. This
arises during convalescence. Although the physician and nurse try to
keep the patient's mind turned outward, inadvertently the necessary
disciplines and procedures tend to cause him to wonder if he will
forever be an invalid.

Consequently a major goal in the pastoral care of the heart patient is to restore his self-esteem. The means by which this is accomplished lies in listening to discover what pursuits or activities
make this person feel he is worthwhile. Perhaps the patient wants you
to see him as a good family man. Talking about this assures him
that he is needed, gives him a sense of belonging, and strengthens
his will to live. If his self-esteem is measured by work, listening to
the patient talk about his job is helpful. The patient may have an

interest in golfing or fishing and derive the same essential advantages from conversation on this social level.

The loss of self-esteem is a common result of any serious illness but is particularly obvious among heart patients. Wage earners, such as the patient described above, fear for the loss of their physical prowess. Professional men, on the other hand, tend to be apprehensive over a possible loss of their ability to inspire confidence in their leadership. For example, a cardiac patient, a minister, was referred to the chaplain because he was seriously considering signing himself out of the hospital against the doctor's orders. Almost in despair he told the chaplain why he felt he must return to his congregation. He was afraid his people would lose confidence in his ability to do the work and would think of him as an invalid. In this instance realizing he would not necessarily be handicapped for life and sharing his ambitions for future growth of his church enabled the patient to accept his illness positively and to receive the maximum benefit of medical care before leaving the hospital.

The pastor should realize that each cardiac patient poses a different set of problems since each individual reacts in his own particular manner. Some react with despair. Others look upon their illness as a test of courage and fortitude. Still others may unconsciously welcome the chance for sanctioned dependency. The preceding discussion has stressed the subjective elements in the experience of the patient: pain, anxiety, and loss of self-esteem.

The inaccessibility of the patient limits pastoral care in cases of sudden heart attack. For example, the chaplain thought it best not to see Mr. Wood until the third day of his hospitalization. Except under unusual circumstances the pastor should not attempt any more than a brief appearance with the patient at this time.

Believe it or not, one pastor who barged into a critical situation stepped out of his role and, holding the patient's wrist, took his pulse. "Good grief," he said, "your pulse is 120!" The physician reported that in a short time after the pastor left, it became necessary to put the patient back under an oxygen tent.

Doctors are intellectually honest enough to admit that a certain percentage of heart ailments may be "iatrogenic," or caused by the doctor. If this is true it seems just as likely that the example given above may be classified as "hierogenic" or caused by the minister!

The pastor's real ministry during the critical phase of the heart attack is with the family of the patient. You will recall that Mrs. Wood said, "This is a great shock to me; he has always been in such good health," and "He's a good man." Both these comments are heard frequently during the early stages of bereavement and illustrate two facts about Mrs. Wood. One, she is in a state of shock, and two, she is reacting to the possibility of imminent death. Good pastoral care of the family will create a climate of calmness and serenity that ultimately reaches the room of the patient. Needless to say this cannot help but add to the efficiency of the doctor and nurse. After the patient passes through the danger period, the pastor will minister to him personally on the basis of his particular needs.

The discussion thus far has been predicated upon the assumption that the patient has suffered a medically documented heart illness. However, more than half of the patients who consult physicians because of heart symptoms do not have any identifiable organic heart disease. Three symptoms frequently presented by patients whose illnesses prove to be functional are sighing, shortness of breath, and an abnormally rapid pulse. Shortness of breath is described almost invariably as "I can't get a breath any deeper than right here," pointing to the upper part of the abdomen. The patient usually first notices his rapid pulse while lying down. The heartbeat is heard in the ear against the pillow, which is normal, but may cause ungrounded alarm. If fear becomes centered on the heart, it tends to increase the rate of heartbeat, producing a vicious cycle. However, "there are many cases of rapid heartbeat in which the usual 'pacemaker' of the heart becomes too rapid. This symptom is not ordinarily emotional, and generally can and must be controlled by administering the proper drug." [2]

A team of doctors completed a six-year study in 1958 of fifty-five consecutive patients with chest pain. In addition to complete physical and psychological examinations, a vast body of social and personal data was obtained on each patient. Three patients could not be categorized. Twenty-five patients had classic heart symptoms for at least six months followed by a well-documented heart attack. Twenty-seven of the fifty-five patients complained of chest pains which they referred to the heart, but had no clinical evidence of any heart disease. The latter group suffered from what is commonly referred to as "functional heart disorder." [3]

The following step-by-step account of the chaplain's ministry to a patient with a functional heart complaint describes something of what the minister can mean to the individual whose anxiety has centered on his heart.

Raymond Harrison, a forty-five-year-old contractor, suffered sharp and penetrating chest pains several days before entering the hospital. The pain in his chest radiating down his arm suggested heart trouble to the patient and his local physician who referred him to a heart specialist.

The chaplain called on Mr. Harrison as a routine visit to a newly admitted patient. His wife was seated beside the bed and in the social conversation that followed she did most of the talking. At the end of the visit Mrs. Harrison thanked the chaplain for calling and asked him to have prayer before he left.

Reflecting upon his initial visit, the chaplain noticed that Mrs. Harrison seemed oversolicitous toward her husband and that he appeared to be somewhat indifferent while she chatted with the chaplain. Since the medical tests had uncovered no organic heart damage, the doctor expressed an opinion that emotional factors were of primary importance in Mr. Harrison's case. The chaplain made it a point to arrange his second visit while Mrs. Harrison was in the hospital cafeteria. He found the patient very communicative: "Well, the doctor said today he had some good news for me; he hasn't found anything wrong with my heart. It's hard to understand how all this pain could come from worry."

"Well, I don't know, Mr. Harrison," responded the chaplain, "the doctors have been saying for a long time now that our emotions do have a direct influence on our bodies. I suspect that all of us have experienced a tension headache or some other bodily symptom at one time or another from the pressure of our work. The thing that throws us off, of course, is that we know we do have a very real pain.

Can you think of any time in the last three or four months, when you have been under unusual tension?"

"I am a building contractor and financially I've been doing pretty well. But I'll have to admit that there is a tremendous amount of competition in the building trade. I usually have several jobs going at one time and maybe pressure does have something to do with my condition."

"It sounds like you are headed in the right direction," commented the chaplain.

"Preacher, you just can't depend on people these days. My foremen come to me with every little problem that turns up." Mr. Harrison clenched his fist as he said, "I get up in the morning ready for work, but by eleven o'clock I'm worn out and want to get where no one can see me. My job is seven days a week. On Sundays the folks for whom I'm building call, and of course I have to do the best I can to try and please them. Before I got into this building business I would visit with friends and sit several hours at a time. I can't do it now. I've got to be on the go all the time. I wake up two or three times a night. Sometimes I get up and dress, go down to the shop to check the doors to see if they are locked, knowing all the time that they are. Something is missing in my life. I wish I could find it. I told my wife last week if I had forty dollars a week and was happy that is all I would ask. I have even thought of speeding in my car and then, jerking the wheel so that it would be all over, but I can't do it when I think of the family."

The chaplain said, "Then you think your life situation might have something to do with your present condition?"

Mr. Harrison said that he most certainly did and that he was seriously considering giving up his present work and selling out. He said, "I think I need to do something less strenuous."

"Of course you will want to give a good deal of thought to such a big decision. Anyway, I think it will help to talk about the tension you have been under in your work," the chaplain responded as he concluded his visit.

The pastor cannot be as aggressive with a patient who is flat on his back in a hospital as he can with a person who seeks him out and asks for his help. The chaplain's opening speech was an effort to structure a relationship that would be meaningful. He attempted to guide Mr. Harrison into looking at himself by creating a climate of going alongside the patient on his journey of self-exploration. He did this both by sharing out of his own life, and by avoiding dogmatic statements about how emotions affect bodily functions.

Apart from the pastor's traditional role as a representative of God, he has probably no more vital religious resource than to lend himself out in the role of a good listener.

Thus far we see a picture that is being repeated in many instances in our culture today, a man caught up in a highly competitive business struggling to manage his labor and please his customers, and finally getting caught in the middle, in this case, with chest pains.

On the third visit Mr. Harrison talked at length about his family background. The essential facts which emerged were as follows: He was the youngest of seven children. "Father was the boss in our family. He told us how to do a job and we were expected to do it right. It was hard at times to keep from getting lickings because I wanted to haul off and tell him what I thought sometime, but I never dared."

Mr. Harrison said he felt closer to his mother than to his father. "Sometimes Mother would fix apple dumpling and she would let me sit and eat to my heart's content. She would let us kids stay up way past bedtime if we wanted to, but father insisted we go to bed by eight o'clock regardless." He added that his mother and father were still living and expressed his delight in being able to send them some of the luxuries in life which they had never been able to afford.

The chaplain replied that he could understand how being used to hard work all his life would predispose Mr. Harrison to taking his work seriously as an adult. The chaplain then asked, "Do you ever have difficulty telling people what you think?"

"I have only fired one person in my life," he replied. "He was a fellow who was doing some painting for me. He did such poor work because of his drinking that I had to let him go. I hated it, because his family needed the money. As a matter of fact, I often dodge my customers. I've gotten so I can't stand to see a client come. I want them to like me, preacher, but they can't as long as I'm like this."

The chaplain then said, "Do you see any connection between not being able to express what you really felt toward your father when you were growing up, and your inability to say what you really want to say many times to your customers?"

Mr. Harrison gave no direct answer, but replied by saying, "Sometime ago my wife and I went on a trip with another couple. I was criticizing his driving, and he turned around and shouted at me. We were paying for the trip, but I liked it that he shouted at me. I had it coming. I admired him for doing it."

In this interview the chaplain not only listened with interest as Mr. Harrison talked further about his background, but also asked several leading questions. His purpose was to direct the patient toward seeing the associations of the past in relation to his present-day responses. In doing this the pastor-counselor should never say "from what you have said then, *this is your problem. . . .*" Such statements as "it seems to me . . ." "I wonder . . ." or "do you think . . ." leave an open end to the question and do not force the individual to a positive yes or no stand. If the patient says "No, I don't quite see what you are talking about," the minister can ignore the point and move on to something else. Later, after other facts come out, an attempt can be made to redirect his thinking to this point again.

On the fourth visit Mr. Harrison talked at length about his own family. He said he had six children. "You know, with my heart condition I can't enjoy the boys and I need to because they'll grow up and I won't know them. I want to run my family like father did his. Hard work in youth never hurt anyone. I told my daughter I'd give her a car and turn her loose at sixteen, but up until that time she needed supervision.

"It costs a lot to raise children these days. And every time I come home they meet me at the door and ask me what I've brought them. My wife and daughter like to shop all the time. I went with them one time, but I couldn't stand it. I had to go to the car. I often get so mad at my wife I could shake her, but you know, preacher, she has a perfect disposition, so meek. When I get all upset she won't say a thing, just goes off and leaves me."

Mr. Harrison kept a bottle of nitroglycerin tablets by his bedside, and up until this visit had always taken several tablets while he was talking. The chaplain remembered this and realized that during this interview he had forgotten to reach for his tablets.

The pastor-counselor who is dealing with a physical manifestation of an emotional problem should continually ask himself the question, "What emotional need is the symptom meeting in the life of the individual?" From the facts which appeared on the third and fourth visits it seems likely that Mr. Harrison has been unconsciously using his heart symptoms to get out from under unbearable pressure. He has talked about how hard he worked as a boy, his strict, demanding father, his oversolicitous mother, the demands of his job, and the strain of parenthood. The heart pain has enabled him to control to some degree the demands made upon him by his foremen, his customers, his children, and his wife. His wife might have earlier walked away from him and refused to work out disagreements, but he is controlling the relationship now.

On the fifth and final visit Mr. Harrison looked more relaxed and was less agitated than previously. He began this interview by saying, "You know, preacher, maybe the church is the answer for me. I am not a church member, but my wife and boys are. I go several months at a time and then drop out for a long while. Up until now I haven't been willing to go all the way. I believe that if you are going to do a thing you ought to do it right and if I join the church I'm going all the way. My parents were strict Baptists," he continued, emphatically. "They were hard believers." He told how his older brother was baptized and "found strength in the Lord for real because it has held up for seven years, so maybe church would change me. I see what it has done for by brother. You are the first person I have talked to about these things. God has been good to me." He paused. "Someone has been. I couldn't have gone this far alone."

"Are you thinking, then, that you don't want to go any further without Him?" asked the chaplain.

"Yes," he said, with tears welling up in his eyes.

The chaplain prayed: "Our Father, we thank Thee that Thou didst love us when we were not grateful. Wilt Thou accept Mr. Harrison with all of his past mistakes and make him to know Thy forgiveness. Give to him the grace to trust Thee and to commit his life to Thee 'all the way.' Help him bear the strain of toil and the fret of care secure in the knowledge of Thy peace, through Jesus Christ our Lord, Amen."

With Mr. Harrison's permission, the chaplain wrote a referral letter to the pastor of the church where his wife and sons attended, suggesting that he could profit by several more hours of counseling. A letter received from the pastor three months later indicated that Mr. Harrison had united with the church, that the minister had seen him on several occasions, and that he was much happier in his new job as the owner of a motel.

The hospital is no place for high-powered, highly emotional evangelism. On the other hand, it affords the best opportunity in our society to link the dynamic power of spiritual healing with the scientific resources of modern medicine. When a person is "yanked" out of a busy life and finds himself staring at the ceiling from a hospital bed, if he ever has serious thoughts he will have some then.

In all probability Mr. Harrison would have resented being asked on the first visit if he were a Christian. Allowing him to talk made it possible for him to realize how his spiritual needs were directly related to his whole life situation. His heart had become for him a symbol for his life.

It is not uncommon among some religious groups to describe religious experience as "getting one's heart right with God." This figure of speech is derived from the Bible where the heart, the seat of the affections, is referred to more times than any other organ of the body.[4] Sincere feelings "come from the heart." We speak of joy as "heartfelt," grief as "breaking the heart," of rejected love as "heart-sickness," and timidity as "chickenheartedness." Hence it is not surprising that many persons tend to focus their anxieties on the heart.

In ministering to persons with functional cardiac symptoms the pastor need not look for a clearly defined "personality type." The crippling effect of this functional disorder varies with each individual, depending upon his personality background and his emotional needs at the specific time in life. Nevertheless there are certain general characteristics of persons exhibiting the functional heart syndrome which the pastor should know.

A majority of these individuals are already convinced that they have heart disease before they ever consult the doctor. "I've been to Dr. Brown, who says there is nothing wrong with my heart, but I know there is," is a typical statement. Before the minister starts helping this individual find another doctor he should let him talk further about his life situation. Chambers, Grant, and White found that in twenty-seven cases of functional heart disorder, fifteen of the patients had never been told by a doctor that they had heart disease, but were as firmly convinced as the twelve who had been erroneously told that they did have heart trouble when consulting other physicians.[5]

The functional group of heart patients tend to run from one doctor to another. In the study just cited the functional group had consulted 4.7 doctors per patient as compared with persons who had suffered actual heart attacks who had consulted only 1.5 doctors.

All persons suffering from functional heart disorder have experienced an emotional upset of one kind or another. Knowing this fact, the pastor will seek opportunities through pastoral visits to allow this person to share his anxieties with him.

Two serious warnings must be heeded in counseling with persons who complain of chronic chest pain. The first of these cautions is that the pastor should never attempt counseling except in direct co-operation with a physician. When he thinks he has information suggesting emotional involvement, the pastor should, with the individual's permission, talk this over with the patient's family doctor. This suggestion takes for granted that the doctor and the clergyman have a professional understanding and a working relationship. If the physician with his technical skill has difficulty in distinguishing organic heart disease from functional heart illness, the minister should certainly not go around labeling every person who is nursing a heart condition as "neurotic."

A second warning is that the pastor-counselor should never attempt to take away the pain-defense of the patient until the person is ready to give it up himself as the counseling proceeds. The chaplain accepted the reality of Mr. Harrison's pain, saying that it was just as real as physical pain, which is true. Extreme resentment and hostility may be aroused by attempting to pry the patient away from his symptoms before he has adequate resources to take the place of the needs which these symptoms are meeting in his life.

The following tragic example illustrates the need for this warning. James Jackson, a middle-aged auto dealer, entered the hospital with chest pain. His business partner had had a heart attack a year previously and wanted to push his son into the partnership. The sales in his business were lower than the previous year and at the same time his wife was elected to a national office of a woman's organization which took her out of town almost half the time. After three days of study the doctors told him he had no organic heart disease. Within six weeks after being discharged he had a psychotic breakdown and was placed in a mental hospital. If this man had had the opportunity to verbalize his anxiety, it is possible his breakdown might have been averted.

Chambers, Grant, and White indicate how much these patients need to hold on to their symptoms by telling of one man who went so far as to secure affidavits, some of them notarized, from friends and relatives to prove the presence and severity of his pain.[6]

In conclusion, it should be said that in some cases both organic and functional heart disorders may exist simultaneously in the same person. Thus, regardless of which factor is primarily responsible for his illness, the cardiac patient needs pastoral care. An effective ministry here may accelerate the healing of the heart both literally and symbolically.

For Further Reading

CHAMBERS, WILLIAM N., GRANT, JOSEPH L., AND WHITE, KERR L. "Angina Pectoris and Angina Innocens," *Psychosomatic Medicine,* 17:128-38, March-April 1955.
———. "The Patient and Physician in Cardiac Symptom Formation," *Journal of the American Medical Association,* 168:1617-22, Nov. 22, 1958.

DUNBAR, FLANDERS. *Mind and Body: Psychosomatic Medicine.* New York: Random House, 1955. Pp. 120-45.

JOHNSON, AUBREY R. *The Vitality of the Individual in the Thought of Ancient Israel.* Cardiff: University of Wales Press, 1949. Pp. 77-88.

MARVIN, H. M., JONES, T. DUCKETT, PAGE, IRVINE H., WRIGHT, IRVING S., AND RUTSTEIN, DAVID D., *You and Your Heart.* New York: Random House, 1950.

WEISS, EDWARD. *Emotional Factors in Cardiovascular Disease.* Springfield, Ill.: Charles C. Thomas, 1951.

WEISS, EDWARD, AND ENGLISH, O. SPURGEON, *Psychosomatic Medicine.* Philadelphia: W. B. Saunders Company, 1957. Pp. 181-224.

TWO *Spiritual Therapy for the Peptic Ulcer Patient*

The association of a full and properly functioning stomach with a contented mind is a very ancient one. Voltaire said, "The fate of a nation has often depended upon the good or bad digestion of a prime minister." C. T. Copeland paraphrased a more familiar quotation when he said, "To eat is human; to digest divine."

Most of us remain relatively unaware of the prodigious activity of our digestive tract. However, it is common knowledge that students before examinations may develop nausea and diarrhea, that businessmen may have heartburn at the time of an important conference or in connection with financial reverses, that housewives develop indigestion when there is trouble with the children, and that children who are not making happy adjustments with their playmates in the schoolyard may have attacks of vomiting at schooltime. This is well illustrated by our general speech—the individual who loses his temper and is forced to "swallow his anger" which he is then unable "to stomach," "stews in his own juice," for which he blames his digestion.

Laboratory observations proving the long-suspected association between emotional stress and profound physiologic changes in the

The authors wish to acknowledge their gratitude to David Cayer, M.D., Professor of Internal Medicine, Bowman Gray School of Medicine and North Carolina Baptist Hospital, for contributing the introductory paragraphs of this chapter and reading the whole for medical accuracy.

stomach as well as elsewhere in the body, make clear the objectives and management of such patients. They must be directed toward the care of the man rather than merely to his stomach.[1]

Until recent years the minister has offered pastoral care to the sick with very little understanding of the individual's personality background. One minister said, "Before I had clinical training in a hospital I simply visited the sick members of my church. They were all sick, so I treated them all alike!" Today the pastor is no more justified in approaching every sick person with the same prayer and consoling scripture than the doctor is in prescribing the same medicine for every patient.

Medical science is accumulating a body of knowledge that can deepen the minister's understanding of the human personality which will result in a more effective ministry to the individual. This chapter attempts to summarize what medical science has to say about personality factors related to peptic ulcer. Then, with a specific case, pastoral care of the ulcer patient can be demonstrated.

By definition, the peptic ulcer is a localized erosion beginning in the inner lining or mucous membrane of the duodenum or less often of the lower portion of the stomach. It forms a sort of crater, which can punch through or penetrate completely the stomach wall. The exact incidence of peptic ulcer is unknown. It is estimated on the basis of autopsy studies that approximately 10 per cent of all persons suffer at some time in their lives from an ulcer.[2] Men are affected four times as frequently as women. Almost 50 per cent of ulcer patients will have recurrence of ulcer symptoms within one year, and 75 per cent within two years.[3]

The outstanding symptom of an ulcer is what the patient often calls "hunger pains" occurring one to four hours after meals, waking the patient at night, and usually relieved by food or antacids. Stomach distress may be present for several years before an actual ulcer develops.

How and why does an ulcer develop? Early studies stressed body type, chemical imbalance, allergy, and focal infection, but these factors are receiving very little attention today. In contrast, the factors constantly discussed today are the muscular activity of the stomach and duodenum, decreased tissue resistance to enzymes, and emotional and physical stress.

The effect of emotional stress on the stomach is mediated through the autonomic nervous system which is not under conscious control. This system is the means whereby the internal organs are regulated and helped to accommodate to changing demands. In the case of the stomach, for example, the sight, smell, or thought of food may result in an output of five to fifteen times the normal amount of highly acid gastric juice. The hydrochloric acid present in gastric secretion has long been viewed as the causative agent in the production of peptic ulcer, but it is actually the end result of a chain of events.[4]

The process by which an ulcer develops has been described in a simplified fashion by Flanders Dunbar.[5] Some emotional disturbance kicks off a large number of nerve impulses which are transmitted to the stomach. This results in the overproduction of hydrochloric acid and disturbance of the even contraction and relaxation of the stomach muscles. The mucous membrane becomes fragile and oversensitive. Any slight break in the mucous-protected lining may be further irritated by the acid and in time an ulceration appears in the stomach wall.

What type of personality is the minister likely to meet in the ulcer patient? Of course, it is always a temptation to categorize people rather than take the time to explore the facts in an individual situation. The physician would be the last person to insist that his patients fit some stereotype even when it is statistically derived.

Yet authorities on the mind-body relationship tell us we are likely to meet a tense, hard-driving individual who feels a compulsion to succeed. As a rule this individual plays as hard as he works, so far as winning is concerned. If he plays golf, for example, and competition becomes keen, the ulcer patient will not profit from his recreation because of his strong desire to win.

Unconscious dependency needs are deeply buried under a successful exterior. The individual compensates for his unacceptable dependency needs by working hard and striving for success wherever he finds himself. Success is satisfying, but heightens his frustration because he is rewarded with increasing responsibilities. Instead of finding relief, he is caught in a vicious cycle.

The story of Frank Thomas illustrates the operation of some of the emotional factors just described and will show how one individual developed a way of life which resulted in an ulcer.

Frank Thomas is a slender young engineer thirty-two years of age. He has been married for eight years and has three children. For three successive years he has been hospitalized for peptic ulcer. At the time of his latest admission he stated to the chaplain his realization that he had been under a good deal of tension. He said his state of mind was not good. As he put it, "I actually think sometimes that I'm mad at God!"

He is the third of four children born into the home of a minister. Both his parents are now living although his father has retired. Frank stated that he saw very little of his father while growing up. On one occasion he hid in the car in order to go with his father to the golf course. His father did let him carry his clubs on this occasion.

His mother was the dominant person in the home. His father had to get her approval before he could even buy a new book for his library. Frank saw her as a strict person. "There was no place for pleasure in her life and so none in mine." Many of the marks of achievement in his life, such as scholastic honors, were won largely out of a sense of duty to his mother who was very ambitious for him. His mother worried because he was thin and was always urging him to eat.

Not until he entered college did Frank have a date. His mother insisted that he go to a small college, and during this time he fell in with the wrong crowd and stayed away from church. Later, on a state college campus he started dating and going with a more wholesome group and soon found his way back to church.

At the state college he felt inferior to his roommate, who was an accomplished athlete. In graduate school he had little time for recreation, taking his vacations to get experience on the job.

The first occurrence of his ulcer came while he was in graduate school in a distant state which was the first time he had been away from home for an extended period. Here he was attracted to a girl who later became his wife. He found her to be a person he could talk to and has depended heavily upon her. "She has really been a second mother to me."

His wife has recently told him that she felt when they were first married that he practically hated his father. The patient admits having some resentment, but denies that it was as strong as his wife implied. For a long while after leaving home he did not write to his parents regularly, but now he tries to send cards and letters frequently. Visits to his parents are still somewhat embarrassing to him because his mother is always trying to do too much for him.

Frank states that he is happily married except for one or two sources of tension. One friction point is over decisions concerning out-of-town business trips which he often schedules without consulting his wife. He fears that if he asks her she will not approve. Usually, however, she goes along with his judgment, but resents being left out of the decision.

Another area of friction involves social activities. He is so consumed by the demands of his business that he has little time for play. He feels that this is hard on his wife who is more outgoing and uninhibited. "She had a much happier childhood than I did, for she knew how to play. In fact ambition is what is killing me. Why can't I enjoy life like the other men in my department? They take time off and go fishing while I am working twelve hours a day trying to set an example."

After being with one firm for four years, Frank took an administrative position with another company which required moving out of his home state. He feels that his executive role compels him to control his life and his emotions to an uncomfortable degree. He has difficulty delegating responsibility: "I guess I'm just afraid to trust other people."

He has always been uncomfortable in the presence of men. This causes problems for him in his supervision of a section of engineers. For example, there is one young engineer in his department who probably knows more about the newer processes than he does. As he says, "I know that if I moved out, this fellow would be put in my place." In relation to his own immediate supervisor he feels the worst tension comes in trying to know when and when not to consult him. "Maybe this goes back to my relationship to my father. He tried to give me money when there were things I wanted, but he gave me very little companionship."

Prior to his latest admission Frank had reached a point of nervous exhaustion. He broke down and cried at small provocation and had a feeling of helplessness which he described as a "nobody-loves-me" feeling.

During his hospitalization Frank received medical treatment for his ulcer and the chaplain in collaboration with his physician saw him on five different occasions.

The facts given above, though somewhat limited, do provide some understanding of Frank's personality background. In tracing these events we find an overambitious mother doling out approval to her son as he attempted to measure up to her standards. Consequently, as a child, his need for acceptance was never adequately met.

As a result of his mother's overprotection Frank developed strong underlying dependent feelings for which he compensated by earning status through academic success. He developed a reputation for conscientious academic work to the exclusion of cultivating social maturity through his college experience.

We see a person leaving home for graduate school in a distant state still feeling strongly the need of his mother's support. As a child his mother was concerned over his thinness and he could gain her approval by eating. Thus, in this stress situation his emotional needs produced a biological overreadiness for food, and his ulcer first appeared.

His wife met some of his dependent needs and for a time his ulcer subsided. He continued, however, to drive hard toward success, and was rewarded by the assignment of heavier responsibility. This resulted in a depletion of his reserves since he was already overextended, and his ulcer recurred.

Frank was not helped any by his father's weakness as a husband and parent. Lacking a strong masculine example, he has had trouble

in maintaining satisfactory relationships with men and this has intensified his problem to this day.

His earliest effort to achieve independence came during his first
year at college when he stayed away from church and, as he said,
"fell in with the wrong crowd." Making decisions without consulting
his wife shows a continuation of this pattern. Likewise, the anxiety
he experiences in relating to his superior and the ambitious young
man under him aggravates his dependency needs.

The pastor needs to have in mind some general idea of what
the doctor will be doing to help the ulcer patient in the immediate
crisis. This will prevent him from working at cross-purposes with the
physician.

The aims of medical treatment of the ulcer patient are three-
fold: (1) to relieve the symptoms, (2) to heal the ulcer, (3) to
prevent recurrences. Usually the doctor will restrict his patient's
activities and with diet, sedatives, antispasmodics, antacids, and reassurance he can ordinarily relieve the symptoms within two weeks.
Conservative medical treatment is usually highly successful and in a
majority of cases results in prompt relief and eventual healing of the
ulcer.

However, permanent victory over the ulcer is a different matter.
Unless the patient can come to an understanding of the sequence of
events which produced his ulcer he is likely to return to the hospital.
Recurrent ulcers with uncontrolled bleeding may lead the doctor
to recommend surgery to remove a part of the stomach.

The pastor can see from the medical goals that in the beginning
of the treatment process he should avoid an aggressive religious
ministry that might agitate the individual.

The aim of the pastor in ministering to the ulcer patient might
be along the following lines: (1) to give support insofar as possible
to his dependent needs, (2) to assist him to come to as much understanding of his own personality as he is willing to undertake so that
he can learn to live in equanimity with his physical limitations,
(3) to help him mobilize his spiritual resources for a fresh interpretation of his way of life.

In order to give support to Frank, the chaplain's first step was to establish a pastoral relationship. As is often the case with the ulcer patient, Frank was an attractive, pleasing person who made an interesting conversationalist. It was not long, however, until the chaplain detected underneath the surface a reaching out for help.

If the minister is aware of the ulcer patient's need for emotional nurture he can be more sympathetic toward any attempt the patient may make to "hold on" to him orally, that is by talking. Sympathetic listening can be an emotional counterpart to the milk in the patient's diet.

Another way dependency needs may be expressed is through a constant seeking of advice, which is characteristic of the peptic ulcer patient. This can be tempting to the pastor or the doctor since requests for advice tend to enhance one's ego. Remember that in the overall process the aim is to help Frank to a better understanding of himself so that he can make his own decisions.

The ulcer patient is no different from the rest of us in that he seldom sees how his immediate frustrations are related to his early childhood experiences. In the beginning the only thing Frank was conscious of was that he had been working hard. But when the doctor discussed with him the relationship between emotional stress and the ulcer condition, he became more interested in exploring with the chaplain the reasons behind his driving nature. On further visits as the relationship deepened, Frank shared with the chaplain enough facts about his background to gain some insight into his life pattern.

One basic rule in pastoral counseling is that insight cannot be forced. Instead, the person must be allowed to proceed at his own speed in his effort to find a deeper understanding of himself. This rule is particularly important in the case of the peptic ulcer patient. The research of such men as Stewart Wolf shows why.

In the case of several ulcer patients Wolf arranged to maintain continuous recordings of the muscular contractions and the acid output of their stomachs. He did this by means of taking periodic samplings of gastric juice, and by placing a balloon in the stomach. Contractions in the stomach decreased the volume of air in the balloon and this was recorded on a moving chart. While recordings of these factors were being made, he involved the patients in a vigorous discussion of significant personal problems. The tracings of his instruments showed that by exposing his patients to emotionally loaded situations, he could induce overactivity of the stomach and typical ulcer pain.[6]

These findings have significance for the chaplain and pastor. Picture a minister, fresh with a new idea of the role of emotions in disease, on his first visit to a newly admitted ulcer patient. He wants to help the patient get to the root of his "problem" so he begins to use a direct question-and-answer method to explore various likely areas of conflict. The minister's probing could result in aggravating the ulcer at the very time the doctor is trying to get the patient to relax and allow the healing process of his body to repair the defect in his stomach.

In the case of a woman patient who confided that she had married her employer following his divorce, a student chaplain with a probing statement replied, "How did you feel about marrying a divorced man?"

Contrast this direct approach with the more relaxed, supportive effect when Frank suggested, "Maybe this goes back to my relationship with my father." The chaplain responded, "You might have a lead there worth exploring."

Generally speaking, in counseling, the minister should strive to stay just behind the growing edge of the individual, aiding him to come to as much understanding of his own personality as he is willing to undertake. Once the patient has come to verbalize an insight then the pastor may lend reassurance and support to counteract the pain which always accompanies growth.

When one is struggling toward a philosophy of life his questions must necessarily move into moral and religious areas. Like far too many persons in our society, Frank has been going through the motions of formal religion with little if any awareness of the relevance of his faith for his flesh-and-blood daily struggle. The minister has a direct opportunity to assist such an individual to relate specific Christian resources to his own inner needs.

Sullivan and Rehfelt have given us a stimulating interpretation of the personality patterns in gastrointestinal diseases. They begin by saying that there are three basic instinctual human drives: The drive for self-preservation (survival), the drive for self-perpetuation (propagation), and the drive for self-extension (domination). While necessary and worthy when indulged in moderation, these needs can if distorted result in sin and disease. The traditional cardinal sins, Pride, Lust, and Avarice, are religious labels for the distorted expression of these needs. Hence the overactivity of the need for survival issues in Pride, for propagation in Lust, and for domination in Avarice. Thus, the besetting sin of the peptic ulcer patient, say Sullivan and Rehfelt, is covetousness. His "needed virtue" is Faith; and the medical advice given him corresponds to the biblical injunction, "Go into the desert and rest awhile." [7]

These spiritually discerning physicians are quite accurate in their diagnosis, and they recognize that religious language is often a much more effective medium of communication with the patient than psychological jargon. However, they are weak in applying spiritual therapy, which is the point at which collaboration between the minister and the physician becomes imperative. Frank Thomas needs to "take heed and beware of covetousness," but it is doubtful that simply telling him this will of itself get at the root of his difficulty.

One ulcer patient shared with his minister his own reaction to this suppressive type of treatment: "If you had given me a self-help religious book the first time you talked with me, I would not have returned. I had read a dozen books like that already."

Only after Frank Thomas has been given an opportunity to pour out or "ventilate" his resentment against his father's weakness and his mother's domination can he come to see their control over his life. Only then can he see that his mother is not five hundred miles away as his conscious mind tells him. She is still with him in his personality affecting his present-day relationships. In striving toward business success and other outward marks of achievement, Frank is still trying to please his mother and cannot enjoy real success when it comes. There is no essential difference in his buying a swimming pool now and making the honor roll in high school when he unconsciously does it as a compensation for his dependency needs. Once Frank comes to an awareness of this distortion in his life he can then accept the positive teachings of religion regarding the eternal values of life.

Jesus dealt with a variety of individuals during his ministry. Does he have a word for Frank's life situation? If we can conclude that this individual is confusing success with self, then his idea of success must be broadened. He must look at life as a whole and not through a keyhole of materialistic values.

Jesus seems to be speaking directly to the ulcer patient when he talked to the man who wanted him to divide his inheritance. He gave a warning that "a man's life consisteth not in the abundance of the things which he possesseth." In fact, the whole passage, Luke 12:13-31, is highly relevant. In the light of a discussion of this passage Frank said to the chaplain, "You know I have been so intent upon providing my family with worldly goods, that I have miserably failed to give of myself to them."

Frank began to see how dependent he really was when he realized that his ulcer first occurred when he moved to a distant state. He said, "I suppose I had just as well admit that at heart I'm still a little boy. This is why just before I came into the hospital I had that 'nobody-loves-me' feeling."

"Do you remember saying when I first saw you that you thought you were 'mad at God'?" asked the chaplain.

"Yes," said Frank, "I see now that I was really mad at my whole frustrating life situation without any real knowledge of why." The chaplain then turned the discussion to what Paul meant in Philippians 4:6-7: "Be careful for nothing; but in every thing by prayer and supplication with thanksgiving *let your requests be made known unto God*. And the peace of God, which passeth all understanding, shall keep your hearts and minds through Christ Jesus." The aim of the chaplain here was to help Frank focus his ultimate dependence upon God rather than deifying his mother regardless of her good qualities.

In spite of the fact that Frank's stay in the hospital was relatively brief, the chaplain helped him to see some of the blockages that were hindering his emotional and spiritual growth.

The Christian fellowship of the church and an understanding

pastor can sustain and facilitate the emotional and spiritual growth of the ulcer patient. Because these people are usually successful in the community, their work load in the church is as likely to complicate their lives as their work load in the business world. Ulcer patients are often found on building, finance, and church promotion committees. An extreme example occurred in one North Carolina church where out of twelve deacons seven had active ulcers at the same time! Likewise, in recent times, peptic ulcer has almost become an occupational disease of the ministry. The righteousness of the cause does not prevent a conscientious pastor from being overwhelmed by the problems of the congregation, church building programs, and like demands. This raises questions about the quality of religious experience in such a setting. The fellowship of the church cannot be a healing influence on the peptic ulcer patient if the demands it makes upon the individual tend to aggravate rather than prevent his illness.

The ulcer patient should be given a place in the organizational life of the church with a moderate amount of responsibility, preferably one where he will be exposed to a good deal of appreciation and support. When the pastor preaches along the theme of "Awake, my soul, stretch every nerve," he should qualify what he says lest the ulcer patient go overboard in his response. Otherwise, he might not feel that he is being fed "with the food that is needful for me" (Prov. 30: 8, rsv).

A concluding word is in order with reference to Frank Thomas. It is not to be inferred that all ulcer patients are as ready to grow as he was on his third hospitalization. By this time he was getting desperate. Oftentimes when the doctor first makes reference to the fact that emotions may be playing a part in the person's illness, the first response of the patient may be to look upon this as a reflection and to resent any interference in his emotional life.

Frank is an ideal example of what an ulcer patient can accomplish if he is willing to face the pain of growth and open up and seek help. It can be reported here that two years have elapsed and he has not kept his "annual date" at the hospital.

In fact, he went home, outfitted his garage with woodworking tools, and now has a much-needed hobby in his life. When his church completed a new building recently Frank took real delight in hand-crafting in his shop the book racks for the pews. He is spending more time with his family and enjoys being superintendent of the young people's department of his Sunday School.

Tucked away within a setting of worldly pessimism in the book of Ecclesiastes is a verse which nevertheless contains a truth the peptic ulcer patient might do well to learn: "Go thy way, eat thy bread with joy, and drink thy wine with a merry heart; *For God now accepteth thy works* (9:7).

For Further Reading

ALEXANDER, FRANZ. *Psychosomatic Medicine.* New York: W. W. Norton & Company, 1950. Pp. 99-115.

DUNBAR, FLANDERS. *Mind and Body: Psychosomatic Medicine.* New York: Random House, 1955, Pp. 163-77.

SULLIVAN, ALBERT J., AND McKELL, THOMAS E. *Personality in Peptic Ulcer.* Springfield, Illinois: Charles C. Thomas, 1950, 100 pp.

————, AND REHFELT, FREDERICK C. "The Spirit and the Flesh," *Southern Medical Journal,* 43:736-43, Aug. 1950.

WEISS, EDWARD, AND ENGLISH, O. SPURGEON. *Psychosomatic Medicine.* Philadelphia: W. B. Saunders Company, 1957. Pp. 289-306.

WOLF, STEWART. "Summary of Evidence Relating Life Situation and Emotional Stress to Peptic Ulcer," *Annals of Internal Medicine,* 31:637, Oct. 1949.

————, AND WOLFF, H. G. *Human Gastric Function.* New York: Oxford University Press, 1947.

THREE *Spiritual Therapy for the Ulcerative Colitis Patient*

The frequency of peptic ulcer and the seriousness of ulcerative colitis necessitate a discussion of these particular illnesses from among a number of gastrointestinal diseases. It is clear from the preceding chapter that the abdomen can be "the sounding board of the emotions." Phylogenetically, the digestive tract is the oldest system in the body and hence is more likely to be used in expressing emotions which can not be dealt with through other channels.[1] The personality types of patients with ulcerative colitis and peptic ulcer present an interesting contrast. The peptic ulcer patient often compensates for his dependency by a vigorous striving for success, whereas the patient with ulcerative colitis tends to be extremely dependent and to have very little drive with which to compensate. There appears to be fairly general agreement as to the personality type in ulcerative colitis.

Nonspecific ulcerative colitis is a serious inflammation of all or part of the mucous membrane which lines the colon. The usual clinical signs are diarrhea accompanied by blood, mucus, or pus with abdominal discomfort or pain. There may be associated fever, loss of weight, and anemia. The disease usually has an acute onset not

The authors wish to acknowledge their gratitude to Marcus F. Sohmer, Jr., M.D., Instructor in Internal Medicine, Bowman Gray School of Medicine and North Carolina Baptist Hospital, for contributing the introductory paragraphs of this chapter and reading the whole for medical accuracy.

infrequently following some emotional trauma. The course is often variable but is usually of a chronic intermittent type.

Therapy is directed principally toward the management of the whole patient rather than the symptomatic complaints. This regimen includes diet, blood transfusions, various drugs, sedation, and a multiplicity of other measures none of which, unfortunately, are specific therapy.

At the present time, this disease is principally treated medically but between 10 per cent and 20 per cent of patients ultimately will require surgical treatment. Surgery is indicated only when there is some complication such as uncontrolled bleeding or when the disease does not respond to medical treatment. Mortality associated with surgery is often quite significant. Emotional adjustment to the surgery required is frequently difficult. The patients need constant reassurance and encouragement.[2]

The emotional make-up of patients with ulcerative colitis has been a fertile field for many investigations since the early 1930's. In general, these people have been described as shy, passive, and withdrawn with a desire to be loved but unable to return affection and express their feelings. They are meticulous and extremely sensitive individuals with a tendency to brood over minor incidents which appear to them to be major insults. This produces marked inner conflicts and consequently patients often have great difficulty meeting everyday problems and adjusting to life in general. Family history often reveals a domineering, abusive, and aggressive father and a possessive overprotective mother. The patient, as a child, learns early to avoid trouble by being submissive and develops extreme dependence upon the mother. Marriage is often postponed by these individuals and when attempted, is often not too successful. In marked contrast to the previously described peptic ulcer patient, ulcerative colitis patients have little drive. They have been described as "subservient but subversive."[3]

There are many people in the general population with the personality characteristics described above who obviously do not have and will not develop ulcerative colitis, so that emotional problems are not the sole factor in the production of ulcerative colitis. It has been suggested that the well individuals have enough emotional protection from their environment to prevent the development of the disease. Some investigators feel that given sufficient time, any psychiatrist can obtain a history from most individuals which contains enough emotional trauma to have resulted in the development of ulcerative colitis. As noted earlier, while many patients will develop colitis following various infections of one sort or another, quite frequently the history is obtained of acute loss of love or disturbing humiliation or other emotional disturbance prior to onset of the disease. Protracted psychiatric treatment is of little value because of the difficulty these patients have in sharing their emotional conflicts. Delayed grief reactions often appear to be a factor in production of ulcerative colitis. In a study of forty-five patients with ulcerative colitis, twenty-six patients were found to have suffered the loss of loved ones immediately prior to the onset of illness.[4]

The following is a typical case history of a patient with ulcerative colitis with associated loss of a loved one and marked inner conflict. J. T., a middle-aged bookkeeper, entered the hospital for the third time in a year with a recurrence of ulcerative colitis. Six months prior to his first hospitalization his wife died. There were no children. He described his wife as "one of the best persons who ever lived. I was completely lost and alone when she died. She paid all the bills and managed the house. She even picked out my clothes."

Family history revealed J. T. to have been "the baby" in a family of three children. He described his mother with almost the identical words he used in describing his wife. His father was an alcoholic who abused the family.

Following his wife's death J. T. began to take his meals at a boarding house near his home. The couple who ran the boarding house had been close friends for several years. J. T. leaned heavily upon these friends after his wife's death and gradual infatuation with the landlady led to an affair about six months after his wife died. Not long after this his ulcerative colitis developed. The husband became suspicious and accused J. T. without any specific proof. In less than twenty-four hours after this scene he was in the hospital with

a severe attack of ulcerative colitis. The patient still had not revealed
to his physician anything about his affair with the landlady.

J. T. expressed a desire to talk to the chaplain after Sunday
service in the hospital chapel. The patient began by saying, "I don't
know how to tell you what I've got on my mind, but I am really in
a jam! I am a church man, but you won't think so after you hear
what I have to tell you." Then he told about the loss of his wife and
his subsequent involvement with the landlady. He was obviously
under a great deal of tension and had marked feelings of guilt. At the
end of his confession, the chaplain reminded him of the scripture:
"If we confess our sins, he is faithful and just to forgive us our
sins, and to cleanse us from all unrighteousness." (I John 1:9). After
a prayer the chaplain walked with him back to his room. Five other
visits were made before he was released from the hospital, during
which time J. T. shared the brief facts about his family background
as given above. The chaplain made no attempt to explore in detail
his personality background but supported him in the forgiveness he
had found and in his determination to act on his resolution to
straighten out his life when he returned home. J. T. stated that the
stress over his involvement with the lady at the boarding house could
have intensified his ulcerative colitis.

The chaplain's ministry to J. T. centered around the events in
his present-day life situation in contrast to a more intensive insight-
counseling ministry which aims at providing an opportunity for the
individual to gain a deeper understanding of his way of life.

There are special problems faced by a patient with ulcerative
colitis which will condition pastoral care:

1. Extreme dependency in the personality of ulcerative colitis
patients is mentioned in every study examined. The dependency pattern of these individuals seems to be necessary to survival since there
is such a lack of ego-strength. Therefore when this dependency relationship is disturbed, they regress in their behavior. A thirty-three-
year-old married man with ulcerative colitis could not move from one
apartment to another without getting his father to look at the new
apartment and tell him whether or not it would be a good idea.
"Proud, vain, and undisciplined," says one thumbnail description,

"these patients have been overwhelmed, humiliated, and defeated, and have retreated into an illness that requires treatment similar to that given a beloved infant, that is, bed care, frequent changes, and baby food." [5]

From the above description it is clear how dependent these people are and therefore how easy it is to become emotionally involved. They are oversensitive, harbor resentments, and are as easily hurt as a child. The pastor should not make promises about return visits or any other commitments he will have difficulty keeping, and should be consistent in his reactions to the patient throughout the relationship.

2. There is frequently a recent emotional upheaval or conflict in the life of these patients preceding the acute attack of ulcerative colitis. In the case of J. T. the crisis was one of guilt over his involvement with the wife of his friend. He finally came to see that his life situation had something to do with his illness and that he must deal realistically with the situation, else his improvement might be short-lived. One study of a number of ulcerative colitis patients showed that a specific conflict situation had immediately preceded the onset in every case.[6] The pastor, therefore, should listen and be alert to any need the patient may have to talk about recent events that are disturbing his dependency relationships.

3. Unresolved grief is often in the background of the ulcerative colitis patient. If J. T. had had stronger inner resources with which to face the death of his wife, in all probability he would not have become attached to the lady with whom he took his meals. Usually when unresolved grief is a factor in the life of the ulcerative colitis patient it is of fairly recent origin rather than having existed over a long period of time. The pastor's role as a minister often facilitates the aiding of the individual to talk about his grief. More often than not this information comes out naturally and normally in conversation. It is socially acceptable, for example, to ask a person whether or not his parents are still living. However, unless the expression of grief is volunteered by the patient, it is wise to refrain from undue exploration with this type individual. In aiding the person to work through his bereavement there is nothing that will take the place of letting

him ventilate his emotions and talk out his feelings. In this way he faces up to the reality of the loss, and can then, in a more mature fashion, build other relationships to support his dependency needs.

4. The main emphasis in the pastoral care of the ulcerative colitis patient should center around his immediate present-day life situation. The weak personality structure and the inadvisability of formal psychotherapy with many of these patients has been referred to earlier. Treatment of the ulcerative colitis patient is directed by the doctor toward physical relief and the return of the patient to his home environment as soon as possible before he becomes too attached to the tender loving care found in the hospital. The pastor also should be cautious about too much involvement and should aid the patient to discuss his present-day concerns in conversation rather than concentrating on his basic personality structure.

5. The ulcerative colitis patient usually operates within a small circle of friends and acquaintances and has difficulty in expressing his inner feelings. In the case cited earlier, it was not until his third hospitalization that J. T. came to share his inner grief and guilt with the chaplain. Detailed personal histories of colitis patients are often difficult to obtain, due to the reticence of these patients. Some time is usually required before the patient can admit any connection between his circumstances and his illness. Hence the pastor can anticipate difficulty in establishing a relationship with the ulcerative colitis patient.

6. Frequent brief visits to the ulcerative colitis patient are desirable. His emotional immaturity is childlike in that he demands more from the people around him than does a more mature person. The pastor along with other members of the healing team can help meet this deep need for affection. Two doctors, White and Selsnick, recommend what they call the "pretty girl treatment" for male patients. Severely ill male patients with ulcerative colitis are to be visited daily by all the pretty female employees of the hospital. "Within a short time the patient changes from a depressed, completely withdrawn, almost hopeless invalid, to one who sits up in bed, shaves daily, takes an interest in his surroundings, and recaptures his will to live." [7]

7. There is always a tendency to probe when working with individuals who have difficulty in expressing themselves. The pastor should be specifically warned against probing approaches to ulcerative colitis patients because of their weak personality structure. The family backgrounds of these patients show a high incidence of psychotic trends, and there is a greater frequency of psychosis among ulcerative colitis patients than among all other gastrointestinal diseases combined.[8] Some authorities go so far as to say that regular psychoanalysis might actually be harmful to some colitis patients.[9] In one hundred twelve patients followed over periods of from one to eighteen years psychogenic factors were recognized, but formal psychiatric therapy was feasible in only a few cases.[10]

Colitis patients often maintain a superficial front and can manage to get along fairly well until a life situation forces them to face their dependency needs and they do not like what they see. Probing, which is thought of here as asking personal questions of an individual in areas of his life which he himself has not brought up, is dangerous since it can result in the collapse of the patient's present system of personality organization. In a counseling situation where the person has requested the minister's help an occasional question close to his "growing edge" is acceptable. But information elicited apart from a relationship of trusted sharing invariably awakens the patient's hostility. As a means of psychic shock probing requires extreme skill and in the hands of a novice can be dangerous. Hence it should ordinarily be left in the hands of a psychiatrist.

8. The ulcerative colitis patient needs a great deal of comfort and support but the minister should give this support in a theological framework rather than accepting personally the dependency that will be directed toward him by this type personality. As opportunity arises, the pastor should ultimately direct the individual's attention and attitudes toward his Heavenly Father. A pastor even on a first visit can say, if prayer is appropriate, "Our Father in Heaven, we thank Thee that we have One who is the same yesterday, today, and forever, to whom we can come in time of need. . . ."

Theological concepts helpful to the ulcerative colitis patient are those which emphasize God's love, forgiveness, acceptance, and

66

mercy, and portray God as all-powerful and purposeful in His plans for man and the universe.

Since the ulcerative colitis patient desperately needs love, but has difficulty loving back, he needs first of all to find someone upon whom he can depend absolutely, and God only can fill this need. Even this dependency relationship should not remain on an infantile level, but should gradually give way to a maturing fellowship of trust which develops in the individual a sense of personal worth as a child of God.

9. The New Testament account of the early church teaches us the inherent power of the Christian fellowship to help both the weak and the strong. The pastor can be the interested person who enables the patient to experience God's comfort and guidance through the supporting community of the church. If the person can be led to become an integral part of one of the smaller groups, such as a Sunday School class, and yet at the same time can be sheltered from undue responsibility, the fellowship of this group may help to keep him functioning which medically is considered successful management of the ulcerative colitis patient.

For Further Reading

BROWN, W. T., PREU, P. W., AND SULLIVAN, A. J. "Ulcerative Colitis and the Personality," *American Journal of Psychiatry*, 95:407-20, Sept. 1938.

GROEN, J. "Psychogenesis and Psychotherapy of Ulcerative Colitis," *Psychosomatic Medicine*, 9:151-74, May-June 1947.

GRACE, WILLIAM J., STEWART WOLF, AND HAROLD G. WOLFF. *The Human Colon*. New York: Paul B. Hoeber, Inc., 1951.

JOSEPH, E. D., WINKELSTEIN, C., AND BROWN, F. "Some Psychiatric Observations of Ulcerative Colitis, *Journal of Nervous and Mental Disease*, 127: 51-57, July 1958.

SULLIVAN, ALBERT J., AND REHFELT, FREDERICK C. "The Spirit and the Flesh," *Southern Medical Journal*, 43:736-43, August 1950.

WEISS, EDWARD, AND ENGLISH, O. SPURGEON. *Psychosomatic Medicine*. Philadelphia: W. B. Saunders Company, 1957. Pp. 278-84.

FOUR *Spiritual Therapy for the Asthma*
Patient

Mrs. X, a fifty-four-year-old housewife, had been in and out of an oxygen tent for five days and nights with a severe attack of asthma. On the chaplain's third visit she asked him to open up the flap on the side of the oxygen tent and said, "Of all the attacks of asthma I have had, this has been the worst. You have been in to see me several times, and I have decided there are some things I'd like to talk about with you."

"If I can help in any way, I'll be glad," replied the chaplain.

In the conversation that followed, Mrs. X revealed a background of strong family solidarity and pride reinforced by strict religious teachings. As a senior in high school, she accepted the attentions of her biology teacher who was ten years older than she. Her family was opposed to his serious interest in their daughter. When she insisted upon marriage, her father in exasperation said, "All right. But don't come whining to me if it doesn't work out."

She was very happy during the summer following their marriage, but in the fall the picture altered. She realized in the midst of wanting to follow the other young people to ball games that she was married to a man burdened with adult responsibilities. The pres-

The authors wish to acknowledge their gratitude to Bennette B. Poole, M.D., Assistant Professor of Internal Medicine, Bowman Gray School of Medicine and North Carolina Baptist Hospital, for reading this chapter for medical accuracy.

tige of "dating the teacher" gave way to the reality of meetings and
paper work brought home at night. Because of her family pride and
strict upbringing Mrs. X had not admitted for thirty-six years to her
family or to any person she was in any way disappointed in her
marriage.

The onset of her asthma came about six months after her youngest son entered college. She was riding down the highway one day
with her husband when they had a quarrel and she had a strong
desire to face her husband with the feelings of disappointment about
her marriage she had kept to herself so long. She controlled herself
but developed shortness of breath and was wheezing by the time
they reached home. She had said to herself a thousand times, "I'll
stick with my marriage until the children are grown." She wept continuously as she poured out her story.

In Mrs. X we see an individual whose loyalty to a rigid family
pattern allowed her no escape from a smothering life situation.
While the children demanded her care she accepted her lot. The
departure of the last child precipitated a crisis in the husband-wife
relationship. During the early years of marriage she had gradually
erected in fantasy what she would do when she had discharged her
responsibilities to the children. When the time arrived, however,
she could not bring herself to sacrifice her security with a husband
she respected for the risk in searching for a love she might never
know. Through discussions with the chaplain Mrs. X gradually was
able to untangle her adolescent ideals of "being in love with love"
from the realities existing in her marriage at fifty-four years of age.
Without being aware of it she had come to care for her husband
more than she realized.

By the next day there was a noticeable difference in the condition of Mrs. X and she was dismissed from the hospital four days
later. Seven years have elapsed and during this time her asthma has
not been severe enough to require hospitalization.

The chaplain's ministry to Mrs. X was primarily confessional
in nature. This confession was valuable in that it met two needs in
her emotional and spiritual life. First, she released the feelings she
had harbored for thirty-six years and the fantasies she had built up

as a result. Second, because of her strict religious training, when the time came to implement her plans for divorce, she was not able to confront her husband. Just as the admission of unhappiness would earlier have caused her to lose face with her family, now a divorce would cause her to lose face with herself. The chaplain's role as representative of God, the church, and her conscience was significant in helping her to resolve this dilemma.

There are certain medical facts which are pertinent to the minister's understanding of the asthma patient. Bronchial asthma is a respiratory condition characterized by a narrowing of the smaller air passages of the lungs resulting in mucous membrane irritation and muscle spasm. The Greek root from which the word "asthma" is derived means "to pant," and describes the wheezing, choking, and suffocating sensation of the patient.[1]

From the time of Hippocrates, who said that violent emotion could precipitate an asthmatic attack, asthma has been considered primarily a nervous disease and was so labeled in older medical textbooks.[2] The causative role of irritating substances like pollen, dust, and food came to be emphasized when the word "allergy" was coined in 1906. Today, according to Dunbar, "the bridge over the chasm between our understanding of bodily and of emotional factors in illness is nearer completion in allergies than in any other field." [3]

The relationship of the allergies and the emotions should be kept in mind in any work with asthma patients. The classical study of twenty-seven asthma patients by French and Alexander concluded: (1) The threshold for allergic sensitivity is dependent on the emotional state of the patient. (2) After the patient has succeeded in overcoming his emotional conflicts he becomes more resistant to the allergens.[4]

The profound influence of the emotions on the respiratory system can be clinically demonstrated. The bronchoscope makes it possible to observe the actual widening of the bronchial passages when pleasant topics are discussed with a patient. The introduction of unpleasant matters into conversation can produce visible constriction.[5] Culturally this knowledge is unconsciously expressed in lay language. When confronted with "breathtaking" experiences of fright or anxiousness we express emotion through a respiratory pattern. Every minister can recall the sighing and crying reactions that take place in the acute stages of bereavement.

Despite the suffocating effect emotions can have on a person, physicians are always cautious until all possible physical causes are eliminated. For example, shortness of breath is not only a symptom of asthma but may point to the presence of a growth in the respiratory system or some heart malfunction.

The minister's concern in the care of the asthma patient as in all other illnesses is in the realm of the emotional and spiritual life of the person. Medical authorities generally agree that there is a great variety of precipitating factors in asthmatic attacks, including almost any sudden emotional stimulus. As one study revealed, "there is no simple psychic *Bacillus asthmaticus*." [6]

Nevertheless, medical research points to a common characteristic appearing in the personality structure of most asthmatics. The central feature seems to be a disturbance of the patient's dependent relationship upon the mother or some mother figure. This dependence has a different connotation from that found in the peptic ulcer patient. The ulcer patient denies his dependence and compensates by striving to succeed. The asthmatic commonly wants to be protected and anything that threatens the relationships upon which he depends is likely to bring on an asthmatic episode.

There are a number of instances in which dependence is unwittingly encouraged by parents. This is more likely in the case of an only child, an unwanted child, or a sick child. In the case of the asthmatic child a vicious cycle may arise after asthma appears. The mother must necessarily attend the child many times in the middle of the night which naturally results in more concern about his general health. The difficult problem in the parent-child relationship is to avoid the child's learning to use asthma to keep his special position with the mother.

A projection of this childhood dependency pattern into later adulthood is seen in the case of Miss J, an eighteen-year-old student nurse who was hospitalized with a severe attack of asthma. The student health officer asked the chaplain to spend some time with her since he thought being away from home for the first time in nursing school might have something to do with her asthmatic attack.

On the first visit she told with a great deal of feeling how an aunt had invited her and her roommate to spend her week's vacation at a mountain lake. Her mother said she absolutely could not do this, but must spend her vacation at home with her. Miss J wanted to spend the week with her aunt but her mother's attitude made her feel guilty over not spending her vacation at home. Yet, she had been home on every free Sunday. She said, "It would be different if I were a long way from home and had not seen them since I entered nursing school. They have visited me on several of the weekends when I had to work."

Miss J was a student in a psychology of nursing class taught by the chaplain. Several hours of classtime had been given to the discussion of personality development just prior to her hospitalization. This furnished a good beginning point to get Miss J to talk about her own family background.

The chaplain saw Miss J each day during the five days she was hospitalized. He learned that she was eighteen months older than her sister, the only other child. Her asthma began at two and one-half years of age. She described her mother as being overconcerned about her as far back as she could remember. This was especially true when she entered the first grade. "I can remember my mother driving me to school, and one day talking to the teacher about my asthma and asking her not to let me go out and play in bad weather." She was more conscious of having asthma during her first year in school than at any other time in her life. She did not complete the grade, but was tutored during the summer and entered the second grade on schedule. "Mother always did everything for us and I suppose my sister and I both are spoiled."

Miss J's asthma continued sporadically through childhood, but declined noticeably during high school. In fact it was not until she entered nursing school that her asthma required hospitalization.

When asked how she got along with her mother, she replied, "She can never please me and I can never please her. If I am at the table eating or when I get dressed there is always some comment which starts an argument." She could not recall ever receiving any more than a slap from her mother.

In describing her father, she said, "He made a good living for our family, but was never very affectionate and he and mother didn't get along too well. They never fussed much in front of us children, but I can remember crying myself to sleep more than one night because I could overhear them fussing before they went to bed. My sister seemed to be closer to my father than I did, and for some reason we always fought. She always wanted to wear my clothes and tag along behind me wherever I went. My sister would often go to Father, climb up in his lap and kiss him good night. I can remember starting upstairs to bed many times and glancing over at him, reading his paper, and longing to go over and kiss him but I never did."

The severity of Miss J's attack declined and she resumed her classwork after five days in the hospital.

Several weeks later just prior to the beginning of her vacation her mother called one night and again insisted that Miss J spend her vacation at home. She told her mother that if she could not spend the week with her aunt in the mountains she would stay in the nurse's dormitory. Contrary to her mother's expectations, Miss J did not go home over the weekend. On Monday evening of her vacation her mother called and began to tell her what an ungrateful child she was. In the course of the telephone conversation Miss J fainted. Her roommate came to her assistance and called the chaplain, who met the two of them in his office and saw Miss J privately while her roommate waited outside.

After Miss J told about fainting during the conversation with her mother, the chaplain said: "Well, Miss J, maybe we had better call the student health officer and see what he thinks about putting you back into the hospital." This came as a shock to Miss J and obviously created the desired effect.

Looking at her, the chaplain continued: "There seem to be only two things you can do. You can either come into the hospital for nursing care or you can go home and crawl into your mother's lap and let her give you a bottle."

By this time Miss J was fighting mad, but she was also assert-ing an independence she had not known before. In leaving the office the chaplain said to her roommate in a joking manner, "The next time she faints, get a bucket of ice water and dash it all over her."

Miss J stood by her decision the remainder of the week, to the amazement of her mother, and in so doing began to establish an adult relationship to her. She graduated from nursing school with-out any other severe attacks of asthma. She later spoke of her mother's pride in the fact that her daughter is a professional nurse. Miss J's mother gained a security in the relationship she had not known while she kept her daughter as "her little girl." Her daughter can now "nurse" her.

All overprotected children do not develop asthma, but when asthma begins in childhood it is frequently associated with a clinging, overprotective type of parent-child relationship. Anytime this parent-child dependency relationship is threatened, the person subject to asthma tends to develop an attack. Miss J's most severe bouts with asthma occurred on three significant occasions. Her first episode came shortly after the birth of her sister which jeopardized her favored position in the family. When she left the sister at home with her mother to enter the first grade her asthma became more pronounced. As she became more secure outside the home her asthma corre-spondingly diminished until in adolescence it had virtually disap-peared. Miss J chose a profession and made a successful beginning but her independence was threatened when her mother attempted to tell her what she could and could not do regarding her vacation. This crisis reactivated her asthma which was a kind of suppressed cry of mingled fear and rage; of fear that she would lose her mother's love, and of rage against her mother's overprotection.

Since dependence is usually at the core of the asthmatic prob-lem, the chaplain consciously watched for the emergence of this pattern in Miss J's relationship to him. On the third visit it became evident that she was developing the same clinging dependence she had known in her relationship to her mother and had wanted with her father. The chaplain was not on time for his fourth visit and she called his office to make certain he was coming to see her. When he did arrive and apologized for being late, Miss J asked if he were not working too hard, showing an interest in his personal life. At this point the chaplain paused and said, "You know, I forgot to tell you this in the beginning. It is my job to represent reality to you to the best of my ability. I am sure there have been times when you were angry enough to throw that water pitcher at me. Have you ever felt that way?"

Puzzled, Miss J haltingly said, "No, uh, I have never felt that way . . ." Looking away, after a long pause, she ventured, "I wonder if I feel too much the other way?"

"You mean, then, you have some positive feelings toward me."

"Yes," admitted Miss J.

"Wonderful," replied the chaplain. "Now that you recognize how you feel we can talk about your needs. Do you remember telling me how many times you had longed to kiss your father good night, but never did? The way we learn to respond to our parents in childhood determines to a large extent how we will respond later in life to persons whom we respect or admire. Can you see how sharing your life experiences with me would revive some of the feelings you had earlier toward your father?"

"I'd never thought of that before," said Miss J, "but I think I see what you mean."

"You realize then," added the chaplain, "that you can't grow at all if you become attached to me in the same sort of way."

From this point and continuing through the last session Miss J talked at length about how painful it is to grow up and learn to trust one's own decisions. The chaplain supported her in her right to have her freedom. In the light of Miss J's bondage to her mother, the chaplain deliberately steered away from the use of religious exhortations which she might interpret as attempts to control her actions. Instead, through his role as a representative of God, he attempted to demonstrate a Christian respect for the sanctity of human personality. The creation of an atmosphere of permissiveness and the provision of support as needed helped Miss J to move toward the achievement of selfhood.

Oftentimes the minister feels that unless he has said something specifically "religious," he has not been true to his role as a preacher. This overlooks the fact that the individual is usually well aware of unfolding his life in the presence of a person charged with religious responsibilities, and furthermore, it is far more important to "be the love of God" to a person than simply to talk about it.

In the big test that came on the eve of her vacation, the chaplain's directive statement about going home and crawling into her mother's lap could not have been used apart from the strong relationship growing out of counseling with her in the hospital. Such directive statements in the beginning of the relationship would only have driven her deeper into her shell.

The following specific points may serve as guideposts in the pastoral care of the asthma patient.

1. The patient whose asthma begins in childhood is likely to be more immature than the person whose asthma appears in adulthood. This is true because of the likelihood of overprotection accompanying childhood asthma and the persistence of emotional difficulty through the formative years. Counseling with Miss J, for example, required a great deal more time than it did with Mrs. X whose asthma had its onset in adulthood. From a practical standpoint the pastor needs to keep this fact in mind as he plans his counseling schedule, because once he lets an individual undertake counseling he is ethically obligated to carry through with the relationship.

2. Moods of depression almost universally accompany asthma. This depression may or may not occur between episodes but is nearly always present during the attack.[7] Ordinarily depression is evidenced by certain manifestations such as exaggerated ideas of guilt, feelings of unworthiness, and a painful sense of failure. The despondent asthmatic, unlike a person in a true depression, can be more easily diverted. Though depressed, the asthmatic maintains good contact with people and only rarely expresses suicidal ideas.

3. Asthma patients frequently have identified with some person close to them who had a respiratory illness. This could be a mother, father, or grandparent living in the home during the formative years. The illness need not have been asthma. In one study of forty nonseasonal chronic asthmatics, more than half had been exposed to

respiratory diseases, usually nonallergic, in people who were important to their well-being.[8] In counseling, this identification with a
significant person is important and should be explored.

4. Crying meets a special need in the patient with asthma.
Medical authorities generally agree that the asthma attack symbolizes
a suppressed cry for the mother. Many asthma patients report that
it is difficult for them to cry.[9] Moreover, asthma attacks frequently
subside after the patient has ventilated his emotions through weeping.

The first case presented in this chapter demonstrates this point.
Mrs. X wept copiously and continuously as she poured out the confession of her lack of love for a man she had lived with for thirty-
six years. Her attack gradually subsided and by the next morning
she was able to breathe without the oxygen tent.

Emotional catharsis or the sharing of one's feelings is recognized as one of the most helpful procedures for the asthma patient.
Because of this the pastor will realize the therapeutic value of crying. Not only will he not do anything to suppress the urge to cry in
his ministry to this type of patient, but in many instances will encourage it when the person is having difficulty in letting himself go.

On the other hand, there can be occasions when the patient uses
tears in an effort to get sympathy or to control the relationship. Self-
pity may also be a motivation for crying. Therefore it is important
to distinguish between the unhealthy and the healthy use of crying.

5. The most difficult emotional and spiritual problem facing
the chronic asthmatic is that of working through his dependency
needs. Simply telling a person he is overdependent or urging him to
"grow up" will not necessarily help him. Like an animal reared in
captivity, a deeply dependent person even when he gains insight will
need a period of support and guidance as he feels his way toward
becoming a person in his own right.

In addition to the creation of a sustained counseling relationship, the pastor may draw upon the Christian interpretation of the
parent-child relationship as a valuable resource in his ministry to
the asthma patient. While the Bible requires respect for parents
(Exod. 20:12) at the same time parents are instructed not to pro-

voke their children to wrath, "but bring them up in the nurture and admonition of the Lord" (Eph. 6:4). The overprotective parent usually fails to admit that he has clay feet. It becomes the job of the pastor-counselor to interpret these Christian principles to the individual in order that he may not feel guilty over breaking these ties and can transfer his ultimate loyalties to God.

The pastor need never be afraid to support a person who is attempting to establish his independence. Invariably when the person achieves his own selfhood his parents become proud of their new-found security. Whereas both parent and child had feared the loss of their love object, through this new birth they discover not only a new freedom but a new love unhampered by unhealthy, guilt-producing ties.

For Further Reading

ALEXANDER, FRANZ. *Psychosomatic Medicine*. New York: W. W. Norton, 1950. Pp. 132-41.

DUNBAR, FLANDERS. *Mind and Body: Psychosomatic Medicine*. New York: Random House, 1955. Pp. 182-98.

KNAPP, PETER H., AND NEMETZ, S. JOSEPH. "Personality Variations in Bronchial Asthma," *Psychosomatic Medicine*, 19:443-65, Nov.-Dec. 1957.

————. "Sources of Tension in Bronchial Asthma," *Psychosomatic Medicine*, 19:466-85. Nov.-Dec. 1957.

TREUTING, T. F., AND RIPLEY, H. S. "Life Situations, Emotions, and Bronchial Asthma," *Journal of Nervous and Mental Disease*, 108:380-98, Nov. 1948.

WEISS, EDWARD, AND ENGLISH, O. SPURGEON. *Psychosomatic Medicine*. Philadelphia: W. B. Saunders Company, 1957. Pp. 428-39.

FIVE *Spiritual Therapy for the Skin Patient*

Elisha's ministry to Naaman, captain of the Syrian armies, is probably one of the earliest examples of the pastoral care of a skin patient (II Kings 5). Elisha sent a servant out to greet him, and Naaman felt slighted. But when the servant delivered the prescription, "Go and wash in the Jordan seven times," he turned and went away in a rage. After Naaman had vented his anger, his servant persuaded him to wash in the Jordan and he was healed.

The clear expression of anger preceding the healing of Naaman bears a striking resemblance to the case of a woman referred to a psychiatrist by a dermatologist. She talked to the psychiatrist at length about her happy home and her satisfactory relationships to her friends and community as though she had no real conflicts. When the doctor informed her that her hour was up she suddenly became very hostile and exclaimed, "You haven't helped me a bit!" In less than a week after she expressed anger toward the psychiatrist she called her dermatologist to say that her rash was clearing.[1]

Both Elisha and the psychiatrist "rubbed the patient the wrong way," which gave rise to hostility. Feelings are often described in everyday conversation in terms that relate to the skin. The sensitive

The authors wish to acknowledge their gratitude to Charles M. Howell, M.D., Assistant Professor of Internal Medicine, Bowman Gray School of Medicine and North Carolina Baptist Hospital, for contributing to this chapter and reading the whole for medical accuracy.

person may be referred to as "thin-skinned" or "touchy"; the insensitive as "thick-skinned." One patient with a skin affliction on his toes said to a chaplain, "I am seriously considering moving my church membership. My pastor does not step on my toes enough in his preaching."

It is generally accepted that skin eruptions due to stress or nervous tension (so-called neurodermatitis) are becoming more prevalent in this age of a fast tempo in living. The appearance of a small itching patch may be hardly noticed initially but this small patch can well be the start of an extensive and persistent involvement of the skin. These rashes invariably itch and the mere act of scratching or rubbing will engender more itching, thus setting up a so-called vicious circle. The more these individuals scratch, the more they want to scratch.[2]

The skin is man's most versatile organ. It covers, cushions, excretes, insulates, and weatherproofs. It transmits such sensations as hot and cold, smooth and rough, sharp and blunt. The infant receives many of his earliest sensations through his skin. Turning red with anger or paling with fear are ways in which inner emotions are registered through the skin.

Although one out of ten patients who consult a family doctor presents a skin problem,[3] it is difficult to sift out the essential medical facts on skin disorders to help the pastor in the care of these persons. There seems to be less acceptable research thus far on the effect of emotions on skin conditions than is true in other illnesses. The nature of the skin as our most complex organ and the wide variety of inner and outer forces converging upon it may account for the lack of agreement by different specialists. Some authorities write convincingly of the part emotions play in various skin conditions, while others are reluctant to say any more than that emotional factors may aggravate the illness or accelerate healing.

One of the most helpful sources of information stems from the research of a psychiatrist and a dermatologist working together.[4] During a given year they studied 17,605 new out-patients seen in a dermatological teaching hospital and found that 45 per cent of the patients exhibited skin conditions in which emotional factors were believed to be important. They examined psychologically and medically groups of patients in a number of different diagnostic categories and analyzed their findings. They report skin diseases to be of two general types: sensation and manifestation.

Chief among the sensory type are the itching or burning disorders such as pruritus vulvae or pruritus ani. The urge to scratch can come from frustrations of a minor nature or from a more intense physical or emotional need. The scratching resulting from the itching can satisfy both erotic and punitive needs. Thomas Carlyle, when asked to name the height of human happiness, replied, "To scratch the part that itches." [5]

Pruritus vulvae, an example of sensory skin disorder, may be due to a variety of causes including irritating discharges or decomposition of urine. In the case of Mrs. W, however, the dermatologist suspected that emotional factors were contributing to the illness and called in the psychiatrist and the chaplain as consultants.

Mrs. W, a forty-two-year-old housewife, was next to the youngest child in a large family. Her mother died when she was fourteen and she assumed responsibility for the home until she was eighteen when her father married again. She felt close to her father and resented his marriage. Soon afterward she left home to marry a man seventeen years her senior. She lived with him two years until he abandoned her for another woman.

"How can a person make such a terrible mistake, when I always wanted a church wedding and a happy home?" asked Mrs. W. "Chaplain," she continued, "I've never told anyone about this, but sometimes when I'm sitting in church I have wondered whether I am living in adultery."

Her greatest concern seemed to be her relationship to her second husband who is six years her senior. Both she and her husband had worked long hours with little time together at home. She decided to stop work because of her skin problem but afterward the itching got worse. Her husband continued working overtime, leaving her at home by herself. On occasions she would go to his place of business and wait for him to close, but he remained indifferent toward her. Mrs. W said, "I love him but I do not know whether he loves me or not. Maybe it's partly my fault, chaplain, I know I've been complaining more lately, and I have not cared about my clothes. I did a better job of housekeeping before I quit work than I do now."

The dermatologist, along with the psychiatrist and the chaplain, worked out a plan of approach. The psychiatrist talked with Mrs. W about the psychosexual problem arising from her close relationship to her father. Her talks with the psychiatrist made her aware of how she had been unconsciously motivated by attempting to get back at her father and to get away from her stepmother whom she disliked. The psychiatrist also explored with her how her sexual desire and the inattention of her husband might be related to the pruritus.

The chaplain attempted to help Mrs. W by showing an understanding into why an eighteen-year-old girl would do what she did under the circumstances. "After all, you did remain with your father and keep the home together for four years," said the chaplain. "If I can see what was taking place in your life and how your emotional needs caused you to marry a much older man, then surely God understands better than either of us, and will forgive our mistakes when we sincerely ask for forgiveness." The chaplain's role personified the concern of religion with the sanctity of the home, so that his acceptance aided Mrs. W to gain relief from her fear of living in adultery with her second husband. Her symptoms subsided, and one of her last statements before leaving the hospital indicates the way in which she was assuming responsibility for her marriage: "I believe that if I will stop nagging, improve my personal appearance, and keep house like I used to that things at home will show an improvement."

Most skin problems fall into the category of manifestations such as rash, lesions, wheals, scales, eczema, and injuries to the surface of the skin. Many of these dermatoses tend to be chronic and recurrent. Mrs. B, thirty-eight years of age, had suffered chronic neurodermatitis for more than fifteen months. During her second hospitalization the dermatologist asked the psychiatrist and the chaplain to interview her.

The chaplain found Mrs. B friendly and intelligent and observed that she was very neat and prim. She has been married fifteen years and has a son seven years old and a daughter fifteen months.

Quite often she asked the chaplain, "Do you think I'm going to get well?" On occasion she referred to other patients in the ward and said, "They need to see the psychiatrist more than I do." Then she blushed and continued, "I'll be all right. I don't see why I can't get along. We have a home, enough money, and everything we need."

She said her friends and neighbors were constantly calling upon her to help them with their sewing. When she does not feel well she gets little sympathy "because no one believes *I* can get sick!" In the hospital she became irritated with another lady in the ward, but was too timid to complain.

The oldest of three children, Mrs. B described herself as much like her farmer father who is hard-working, punctual, and perfectionistic. She telephoned her mother every day while in the hospital and said that she felt closer to her than to her father.

The psychiatrist described Mrs. B as rigid and perfectionistic. He told the chaplain that when he urged her to socialize more and mix with other people, she replied, "I can't do that unless I start going back to church."

In discussing her church life with the chaplain Mrs. B said she felt guilty over not attending church as she was brought up to do. She had not been out of the house for any social activity during the past year and a half, her reason being "no one can take care of the house and the children like I want them to." She seemed to take great pride in telling how hard she worked on her yard and in the house. "I like things just so and can't stand dirt. My husband says if there's nothing to clean I will turn the bed over just to straighten it out."

On another interview Mrs. B said taking care of the children was a big problem to her. She stated further that her present skin problem developed a few months after the birth of the youngest child. "I love my children," she said, "but they are a lot of trouble. The baby is a sickly child and demands a lot of attention. The way things are now I can't even pick her up." As she said this she held out her arms which were covered with rash. She was disturbed because her husband gave so much time to his work with a sick child at home.

"He simply will not sit down and talk these things out with me," she said.

Mrs. B had worked in a textile mill from the time she was eighteen years of age until shortly before the birth of her last child. She liked her work and found satisfaction in the pressure of its routine. The coming of the second child and her subsequent skin condition had compelled her to withdraw from work outside the home.

During hospitalization her dermatitis cleared up and she told her doctor that she "felt free" for the first time in many months. He suggested that it might be a good idea for her to return to her job in the mill. Mrs. B readily agreed and declared that "after working all your life it is hard to change overnight."

When this case was presented to the chaplain-intern staff conference the dermatologist concluded the discussion by saying:

"On a return visit Mrs. B reported to me that her daily living had become more varied and enjoyable and that both she and her husband had started attending church regularly. The most important criterion of success in my specialty is the permanency of the improvement. She has more than passed this acid test since her skin eruption has not recurred over a period of many months. In my opinion the team approach was of inestimable value in Mrs. B's case."

Although the psychiatrist suspected that the underlying problem in Mrs. B's case was unconscious rejection of the baby whose coming caused her to stop work, he made no attempt to explore this because of the brevity of her stay in the hospital and her very rigid personality characteristics. One cardinal rule in counseling is that an individual's thinking is never directed into an area of conflict unless there is adequate time to work through the problem. This means that those working together to help the patient must first of all evaluate the degree of the patient's emotional involvement and then determine the depth of the approach to be made.

Upon the first visit the chaplain found Mrs. B discouraged and wondering if she would ever get well. He readily agreed that he could see why she would be exasperated with an illness that had dragged on for fifteen months. It is a help to any sick person to sense that his own anguish is understood by another. When the chaplain "lends out his emotions" in this way he enables the patient to feel that someone else has looked out at the world through his eyes. Listening with sympathetic interest is the best way to render needed support.

Because of Job's skin condition, his friends scarcely recognized him. "They sat down with him upon the ground seven days and seven nights, and none spake a word unto him: for they saw that his grief was very great . . ." (Job 2:13, ASV). Regardless of any criticism which might be directed toward the theology of Job's comforters they had the good sense in the beginning to listen to him without any hasty attempt at reassurance.

The exploration of her church relationship constituted the second phase of pastoral care with Mrs. B. Knowing her to be a compulsive, perfectionistic type of person, the chaplain realized she was already condemning herself for not having attended church in the past fifteen months. He listened with understanding as she explained how self-conscious she was of her arms in public, which seemed to relieve her guilt, and he left her looking forward to renewing her church relationship now that the rash had cleared.

Generally speaking, the pastor should keep the following facts in mind as he ministers to patients with skin disorders:

1. The skin is a symbol of the whole self. Satan voices this in the book of Job when he says: "Skin for skin, yea, all that a man hath will he give for his life" (2:4). Anything that affects the skin tends to influence the whole personality. Even a common thing like acne can cause untold suffering to the adolescent, disturbing his social adjustment. In this connection Charles Howell points out the wisdom of carefully avoiding the term "disease" when referring to a patient's skin eruption. Many patients tend to be extremely sensitive about the suggestion that they are afflicted with a "skin disease" and serious harm can come from the innocent use of such a term. We have found a good response to the use of the expression "skin problem" while talking to a patient. To be aware of how intense are the feelings connected with skin conditions should help the pastor to move delicately in establishing a relationship with the person.

2. People with skin disorders tend to be friendly and receptive

to the pastor's interest but at the same time may possess underlying hostility. In some cases the patient's need for acceptance is so intense that it almost verges on exhibitionism. When Mrs. B showed the chaplain her rash, she crouched over holding out her arms in the attitude of a supplicant. A further indication of the need for approval and acceptance is the frequency with which the skin patient will shift the subject of the conversation away from himself and toward the chaplain. The pastor will strengthen his relationship to such an individual by sharing something of himself and his interests when the patient requests it.

3. Skin diseases, possibly more than any other affliction of the human body, tend to deface the person's ego or damage his self-esteem. Many patients feel that their skin condition is nasty, dirty, and infectious. One specialist has warned the general practitioner at this point that questions about whether his illness is malignant, scarring, infectious, or venereal may be of more importance to the patient than the name of the disease itself. Therefore, he recommends that the doctor take the time to allow the patient to ask these questions and give factual reassurance.[6] Because of his loss of self-esteem, the patient needs to be loved and not loathed.[7] One skin patient said to the chaplain, "I guess what I need more than anything else in the world is to be loved."

4. The loss of one's self-esteem leads naturally to a sense of isolation. A painful consciousness of skin conditions which are obvious and ugly may tempt the person to withdraw from normal social contacts. When the pastor encounters an individual with an exaggerated skin condition he is looking at a person who in New Testament days would have been cast out of the community and compelled to cry, "Unclean, unclean!" [8] The fact that Mrs. B imposed a fifteen-month exile upon herself testifies to the intensity of her suffering. Therefore, the pastor needs to guard against giving off through his expression any feelings of revulsion that may be aroused by the skin disorder.

5. Eczema is one skin disorder where there seems to be a growing concensus of opinion about the importance of anger as an underlying factor. About one-third of all patients who see the dermatologist

have conditions loosely described as eczema.[9] The word "eczema" literally means "a boiling over." One study of five eczema patients who were given intensive group therapy in two hundred tape-recorded hours established two conclusions. The build-up of hostile tension was associated with outbreaks of rash. The releasing of anger in the permissive group was accompanied by a subsiding of the rash. Over a period of six years the relation of emotional changes to skin changes was consistent.[10]

In the light of this present-day medical research it is interesting to resurvey Job's experience. As he vascillated between submission and rebellion toward God, Job exclaimed, "My skin closeth up, and breaketh out afresh" (Job 7:5, ASV).

The pastor should be aware that an overfriendly reception of his role can be a mask to hide pent-up anger. One patient was so hostile toward her physician for allowing "a nervous patient" to be in the same room with her that she nearly lost her voice. She followed the chaplain to the end of the hall and began to whisper her indignation. Her voice became noticeably stronger as she expressed her hostility. This illustrates the inability of the skin patient to express his anger effectively, that is, to the person directly involved. Hence, any time there is an indication of hostile feelings, the pastor should encourage the expression of these emotions.

6. The skin patient usually has difficulty in accepting the idea that his emotions have anything to do with his illness. Almost invariably the patient himself is not conscious of being under stress although a member of the immediate family will frequently tell the physician of the existence of nervous tension. The patient's awareness of stress is often of very definite benefit in successfully treating the dermatitis. In functional heart disorder the patient knows he has a pain, but the cause, organic or otherwise, is invisible. In contrast, the patient with a skin disorder not only feels the discomfort but can see the skin lesion itself. This calls for skill and patience in guiding the person to accept the fact that his emotions may be vitally affecting his skin disorder.

In summary, then, the possible existence in the skin patient of ego-damage, discouragement, social isolation, and repressed hostility furnishes clues to some likely avenues to be followed in an attempt to make pastoral care relevant to the patient's specific needs.

For Further Reading

BIRD, BRIAN. "Certain Observations upon the Relationship of Anger and Eczema," *American Practitioner and Digest of Treatment.* 9:929-32, June 1958.

KÖHLER, LUDWIG. *Hebrew Man.* London, SCM Press, 1956. Pp. 56-57.

MADDIN, STUART. "How Important Are Psychosomatic Factors in the Field of Dermatology?" *Canadian Medical Association Journal,* 77:555 f., Sept. 15, 1957.

RUSH, STEPHEN, *et al.* "Neurodermatitis and Emotional Tension," *A.M.A. Archives of Dermatology,* 76:766, Dec. 1957.

WEISS, EDWARD, AND ENGLISH, O. SPURGEON. *Psychosomatic Medicine.* Philadelphia: W. B. Saunders Company, 1957. Pp. 478-94.

WITTKOWER, ERIC, AND RUSSELL, BRIAN. *Emotional Factors in Skin Disease.* New York: Paul B. Hoeber, Inc., 1953.

SIX *Spiritual Therapy for the Migraine Patient*

Headache is estimated to occur in 50 per cent of patients consulting physicians, being exceeded in frequency as a symptom only by constipation.[1] The writers of television commercials must be aware of this since they seem to assume that all Americans are plagued by headache.

Since headache may originate from many sources, the physician is faced with the problem of determining whether it is caused by such factors as a blow on the head, eyestrain, sinusitis, brain tumor, muscular tension in the neck, or nervous strain. A distinct type of headache affecting 8 to 12 per cent of patients seen by general practitioners is known as migraine.[2]

Galen (A.D. 131-201) is believed to be the first to use the term hemicrania (half skull) in recognition of the characteristic pain on one side of the head. The word was successively changed to hemigranea, emigranea, migrainea, and migraine. Popular use of the word migraine is broader than medical use, and "migraine" today is a fashionable disease often used as an acceptable excuse for evading social responsibilities. The picture of migraine from the medical standpoint is a recurrent, severe, one-sided headache often preceded

The authors wish to acknowledge their gratitude to Martin Netsky, M.D., Professor of Neurology, Bowman Gray School of Medicine and North Carolina Baptist Hospital, for contributing the medical picture of migraine and reading the whole for accuracy.

by disturbances in vision, accompanied by nausea and vomiting and followed by sleep. Migraine occurs in persons who are in good health between attacks. A history of a similar disorder is often present in other members of the family. There are, however, many variations in the disease. The visual changes may be in patterns of bright lights or falling stars, and medical historians have suspected that "visions" in the past may have occurred in some migrainous persons. Sydenham (1624-1689) said the condition affects "wise men more than fools," but the intelligence of these patients is not reflected in their reactions to life. Professional people, including physicians and ministers, are frequent victims! [3]

Migraine is more common among persons fifteen to thirty-five years of age and occurs at intervals varying from two or three times weekly to once a year.[4] According to Wolff, the pain of migraine is caused by enlargement of the arteries on the outside of the skull. Supporting his theory is the relief from pain which follows the injection of ergotamine tartrate, a drug causing sustained contraction of arteries. In a study at the Mayo Clinic, migraine was found five times more often among patients with hypertension than in a control group without hypertension.[5] Hypertension also may be accompanied by a disseminated constriction of the blood vessels. The opening and closing of these blood vessels is largely under the control of the autonomic nervous system.

The descriptions of the personality structure of the migraine patient as found in medical literature are of interest to the minister. In an early attempt to define "the migrainous personality" Touraine and Draper studied fifty patients.[6] They found that the migrainous patient tended to be above average in intelligence, but was retarded emotionally. They noted that the attacks were related to situations in which the individual was forced to stand alone and assume adult responsibility. Differentiating between true and pseudoheredity, they found the unconscious imitation of a migrainous mother to be a causative factor. Because migraine responds to so many different treatments, they concluded that the disorder is comparable to any other neurotic illness and that psychotherapy is the treatment of choice.

Marcussen and Wolff depict the migraine patient as a person with unusual ambition, excessive competitiveness, meticulous perfectionism, rigidity and compulsiveness, inability to express hostile impulses adequately, and a varying degree of impotence in men and frigidity in women. "The outcome of this way of life is resentment, fatigue, tension, hostility, and exhaustion." [7] Essentially the same compulsive traits of migraine patients were found by Ross and McNaughton in a controlled group using the Rorschach method.[8] The rigid schedule these people follow causes them to resist strongly any change of pace. Simply starting back to work after a holiday may impose enough stress to bring on a migraine attack.

In a psychoanalytic study of eight migrainous patients, Fromm-Reichmann found marked unconscious hostility toward a person to whom the patient was closely attached.[9] Conscious devotion and unconscious resentment, she thought, occurred because the patient usually comes from a family with strong solidarity and family pride. In such a family structure aggression is not tolerated. If a child expresses hostility he is likely to be ostracized from the family. The fear of being cut off from the family controls the child and thus requires him to turn his rage inward upon himself. Later in life the mixed feelings are transferred to other persons in authority and when hostility cannot be expressed adequately, it may result in an attack of migraine.

These studies provide clues to the basic frustrations facing the person suffering from migraine. The reader will understand by now that case material in this book is not presented for the purpose of proving any causative relations between emotions and bodily illness. Rather, the purpose of the case material is to demonstrate pastoral care as it is affected by the specific personality factors generally accepted by medical science to be related to the illness.

Mrs. M, twenty-four years of age, came into the hospital complaining of a severe headache. Three months prior to admission, while she was doing the family laundry, one of her twins in the play pen screamed. As she turned to investigate, she experienced spots of light before her eyes, later followed by the worst headache she could remember. Similar headaches had recurred at least once a week since that time. Late in the afternoon on the day of her admission she asked the nurse to call the chaplain to read to her. When he arrived, he found her lying in bed with a wet cloth covering her eyes and forehead. After getting acquainted, Mrs. M said, "I always read my Bible daily, but I do not feel like reading today because I have such a headache."

The chaplain asked if there were any particular passage of scripture she would prefer him to read. "Yes," she said, "read the sixth chapter of Ephesians, where it says 'be strong in the Lord, and in the power of his might. Put on the whole armour of God. . . .' That passage has always meant a lot to me." The chaplain read the requested scripture, offered a supportive prayer, and said as he left, "I'll be seeing you when you're feeling better."

On the following morning the chaplain consulted the resident doctor about Mrs. M. After X rays and other extensive tests, the doctor stated that in his opinion her headaches were of a migrainous nature and asked the chaplain to work with her.

In four subsequent interviews Mrs. M shared with the chaplain the facts that are presented in the following outline of six major areas of personality development.

Family Adjustment: Mrs. M is the middle child in a family of three girls. One sister is five years older and the other two years younger than she. The patient stated that she was "her father's girl" and she loved him because he was good to her but her mother was mean to her. She felt that her mother favored her youngest sister "because she was pretty and nice and clean, and I was ugly and mean as the devil." Her mother whipped her frequently, but she could recall but one occasion when her father had punished her.

The patient said her older sister had always seemed like a mother to her, but that she had always resented her younger sister. Everyone seemed partial to this sister except her father. She related with intense feeling how when her uncle came to visit he would play with the pretty younger sister, but would turn to the patient and say, "I don't see how you can be so damned ugly!"

Since she can remember, she wanted to be a boy. When she was about five years old she heard a preacher say that if one had faith the size of a grain of mustard seed he could remove mountains or have what he wanted. That night she prayed to God to change her into a boy and her dress into a pair of overalls. The next morning when she saw she was still a little girl and had her dress, she cried and "cursed." Today she still wears blue jeans and her husband has to buy her dresses.

She spent a great deal of time with her father, helping him feed the chickens, work on the car, or whatever he was doing. She asked for a knife or air rifle for Christmas instead of a doll. When she received dolls, she refused to play with them. "I would take my knife and cut it up, and take out the piece that says "Mama!"

Today her mother feels that the patient has made a better adjustment and has more friends than her sister has. "My mother is a sweet Christian woman."

School Adjustment: Mrs. M always turned in perfect papers in school. First she would go to the wastebasket and get scrap paper on which to work her problems; then she would transfer them to a clean sheet. She took an interest in arts and crafts, and remembered how when she made a mistake in crocheting she would unravel it and start over.

Mrs. M completed nine years of school as compared with six for her husband, but she has read widely and gives the impression of having a college education. She said she "usually knew more" than the people with whom she associated. "They would not understand the things we are discussing," she told the chaplain.

Social Adjustment: Most of Mrs. M's childhood playmates were boys, and even today she seems to get along better with men than with women. She got along well with the people she met while working, but she has little in common with the other women on her street whom she describes as doing nothing but gossiping all day.

Vocational Adjustment: The patient got along well as long as she was working outside the home but derived little satisfaction from her role as housewife and mother. Mrs. M left the impression with the chaplain that she was so compulsive about having everything "just so," that housework was a burden to her.

Marital Adjustment: At seventeen, Mrs. M married a man

twenty-seven years of age whom she described as "good and kind and the best man she ever knew." She worked outside the home until her twins were born. About three months before she entered the hospital she said the twins began to get on her nerves to the point that she sometimes lost control of herself and threw things at them. "When they would dirty their diapers I would rub them until they were raw just to make them cry," she said, and sobbed uncontrollably for several minutes. Her mother and pastor said it was the devil in her that caused her to do it. She said she did not do a thing like this until her headache almost blinded her.

Mrs. M always dressed her twins alike. "One is pretty and sweet like my younger sister. The other is ugly and mean as the devil, like me." On one occasion she made dresses for them and one of the dresses was prettier, so she put it on the pretty twin. Then she felt guilty about being partial, took the dress off, and put it on the other twin.

Religious Adjustment: Mrs. M was converted three months before entering the hospital and joined the Holiness Church. She brought her Bible to the hospital and read it daily except when her head ached too badly.

"Everything always has to be just right," Mrs. M said. "I cannot stand it when things are not right." When asked if her religion did not expect her to be perfect, too, she admitted that her religion teaches "we can live above sin. If I didn't believe that, I wouldn't have religion." The chaplain asked how her religion had been of help in her present situation. Mrs. M replied, "The trouble is not my religion, it's that half of me wants to do right and half of me wants to be mean." She then remembered a song she used to sing as a little girl: "Half of me says get religion; half of me says be low down. Sometimes I'm singing 'Glory, Hallelujah!' Next thing I know I'm going to town."

Her mother and preacher told her before she came to the hospital that she was possessed of the devil "just like in Bible times." In speaking of the last time her minister visited in her home she said, "I hoped he would never come back. That wasn't right, was it?"

Her husband did not want the minister to visit the home because it upset her.

The facts in Mrs. M's case are set forth under six major areas in order to demonstrate clearly the importance of personality development for pastoral care. It is a good sign when early in his training a student chaplain remarks, "I have all these facts, now what do I do?" Such a remark reveals: that the student is searching for a disciplined framework of personality development against which to see the facts; that he must learn to distinguish between symptoms and causes of human behavior; and finally that he is underestimating the therapeutic value of sharing the intimacies of one's life with a representative of God.

Mrs. M's pastor had no problem about what to do with the facts of her life, because he did not take the time to get even this far. He simply imposed upon her a legalistic theology; and she said she hoped he never came back.

Religion cannot become a dynamic force in any person's life until it has penetrated the depths of the personality pattern and been appropriated to the areas of basic need. Many times the individual has blind spots that hinder this process and can only gain insight through the warmth of Christian love mediated through someone who cares.

In order to understand Mrs. M it is necessary to examine the formation of her personality in early childhood. Her concept of herself was affected by rejection on the part of her mother, competition with a pretty baby sister, and overidentification with her father. Her feelings of rejection stemmed from the fact that her mother showed partiality toward the baby sister. The clash with her mother led to whippings. Childhood hostility was expressed by cutting up the doll and taking out the piece that said "Mama."

The product of this experience was the development of ingrained hostility toward the mother and the sister. Unable to compete successfully with her sister in looks, as her uncle cruelly reminded her, she excelled in her schoolwork. The only persons in her family left to turn to were her father and older sister. Out of this family background emerged personality characteristics that carried over in every area of her life. In her school adjustment she was over ambitious and perfectionistic. She was intelligent, read widely, and excelled those around her. Mrs. M's social adjustment reveals her close identity with her father in that she preferred to play with boys and in adulthood got along better with men than with women. Her lack of identity with her mother explains her unhappiness in the vocational role of a mother to her own children. Her fastidious housekeeping is a further evidence of her compulsive tendencies. It is obvious from her marital history that her husband possesses many of the same characteristics of her father. One might also surmise that her early marriage was an effort to escape an unhappy home situation.

She made a fair adjustment in marriage until she entered into the role of motherhood. The birth of the twins created added responsibility and placed more stress upon Mrs. M than she could bear. The irony of this situation lay in the fact that the twins were flesh and blood mirrors of her basic conflicts. She was compelled to bathe, dress, and care for twenty-four hours a day the twin girls who epitomized the most acute pain she had known in the formation of her own personality: "One is pretty and sweet like my sister. The other is ugly and mean as the devil, like me."

The quality of Mrs. M's religious experience paralleled her personality characteristics. Like all of us, she responded selectively to those aspects of religious teaching which best met her emotional needs. Mrs. M was very defensive when she said, "We can live above sin. If I didn't believe that I wouldn't have religion." She had used her religion to reinforce her perfectionistic tendencies rather than face the painfully contradictory elements in her emotional life.

Mrs. M was dismissed from the hospital after five days. Her immediate attack had subsided. She lived two hundred miles from the medical center and there was no follow-up of her case. How much help of a permanent nature Mrs. M derived from her interviews with the chaplain can only be conjectured.

However, the chaplain definitely felt that Mrs. M gained some insight into her basic way of responding to life situations. His ministry to her began on a supportive level. After the doctor focused her

attention on her emotional life she moved rapidly into a discussion
of her family background. She was able to see how the birth of her
twins revived the deep resentment she had carried toward her sister
and mother thus far in life, and made the statement that she believed
she could be a mother to her twins now without projecting her own
hostility upon them.

Probably no one knows better than the pastor that hate, bitter-
ness, envy, jealousy, and malice have a way of eating at the soul as
disease eats away on human tissue. Any strong emotion such as hostility is difficult enough to handle when it is conscious. It is even
more difficult to deal with when it has been repressed since early
childhood and is affecting the adult in an unconscious way. For this
reason, an effective ministry requires sensitivity and skill. The pastoral care of the migraine patient may proceed along the following
lines:

1. Pastoral visits should not be attempted while the individual
is in the midst of a migraine attack. One migraine patient said to the
chaplain, "It is the sickest sick there is. I did not want to see anybody, not even my best friends!" By showing consideration the
pastor will strengthen his relationship and increase his chances of
being helpful after the attack has run its course.

2. The migraine patient should be encouraged to talk about
his attack and the events in his life which immediately preceded it.
In one study a detailed history of the events of the twenty-four hours
preceding the headache was obtained from twenty patients. "In
almost every instance there occurred an episode to which the patient
reacted with rage and resentment to which he was unable to give full
expression." [10]

3. The pastor should aid the migraine patient to ventilate his
emotions. Marcussen and Wolff go so far as to say that "situations
that dispel tension, relieve anxiety, and dissipate the effects of frustration and resentment" can "modify the course of a patient with
migraine. Dispelling guilt and conflict through interviews can diminish the frequency and intensity of attacks." [11]

4. The pastor should be careful to support the migrainous
patient who is expressing hostility. The perfectionistic person has

difficulty in expressing these feelings. To preach at these individuals the moment they begin to verbalize their resentments is to fall into the pattern of the mother or father who forced them to repress their feelings in the first place.

Often when a person voices resentment toward a member of his family to an outsider, he feels that he has let his family down and will usually follow this by telling the pastor about some of their good qualities. Notice that Mrs. M spoke of her mother as "a sweet Christian woman."

On such occasions the pastor-counselor may say, "Your purpose in talking with me is not to tell me about the picnics you went on and all the good times you had while growing up. These experiences were not problems to you. Since none of us is perfect, what we are trying to do here is to untangle the good qualities of your mother and father from their weaknesses. Then you can love the good all you want to and hate the bad all you want to. In the past you have not differentiated between the good and the bad, and therefore have been emotionally blocked from doing a good job of either."

5. Simply expressing hostility is not enough. Too many counselors have falsely assumed that just to get an individual to ventilate his hostile feelings was sufficient. There is a real question whether or not the latter state is not worse than the former. There is no virtue in simply being able to verbalize resentment about a parent's weakness and stopping here.

After a person has sufficiently verbalized the hostility the pastor may say, "Tell me something about your mother and father's background." Every person knows some facts about their parents' childhood. Having discovered some of the "whys" behind his own behavior, the counselee can see his own mother and father in a larger perspective. This may be called "getting the long look" into the human race and helps the individual to rise above the immaturity of his past actions. Getting the long look, then, into the polluted stream of unhealthy emotional reactions in the human race leads one to desire to rededicate his life and to pass on to his children as little contamination as possible.

6. The migraine patient basically faces the problem of learning

how to handle hostility in a socially acceptable fashion. Unleashing it upon himself can lead to illness, and viciously directing it upon others disrupts society.

The migraine patient may learn from the example of Jesus that it is possible to "be angry and sin not." In the cleansing of the temple Jesus personified two practical principles for the healthy handling of hostility, neither of which was repressive.

In the first place, he deliberated before he acted. He inspected the temple precincts in Jerusalem and must have had some feelings at the time, but returned to Bethany and slept before chasing the thieves out the next day (Mark 11:11-16). His deliberate action was aggressive, but not impulsive. Impulsive anger always leads to trouble. As the Hebrews were wont to say, "He that is slow to anger is better than the mighty; and he that ruleth his spirit than he that taketh a city" (Prov. 16:32).

In the second place, he had a just cause for being angry. The most frequent objects of his hostility were hypocrisy, legalism, and the injury of human personality. There is enough evil in our society to furnish sufficient avenues for the channeling of hostility. Mrs. M had to learn first of all to accept her anger as a fact. She was able to do this by seeing that she was justified in being hostile toward the evil in her parents at the same time that she was justified in loving the good in them.

7. When the pastor studies intensively the past life of a person like Mrs. M he cannot help but become interested in preventive measures. Past generations placed emphasis upon suppressing hostility in the child, rather than teaching him how to express it in an acceptable manner. The watchword of this philosophy was, "A child should be seen and not heard." The first reaction against this tradition said, "Let the child express his aggressive feelings." It did not take the pendulum long, however, to swing back between the two extremes.

Teaching parents how to respond to specific instances in childhood behavior is not easy but it affords the only way to produce healthier personalities. An example of one parent's response to hostility in his child can serve as an illustration. On a rainy afternoon, a father who had overslept was hurriedly packing his suitcase to drive to a distant city. His eight-year-old daughter was bouncing a rubber ball all over the place, and he had asked her twice to stay out of the way. When the ball finally landed in the suitcase he said in a gruff voice, "I told you to take that ball into another room!" Before going to the car he kissed his wife and son, and turning to the daughter who was standing glumly off to the side, he asked, "Aren't you going to kiss me goodby?" Her reply was, "Go get yourself killed!"

The father was already anxious over the dangerous driving conditions, and this remark shocked him into a rapid consideration of how to respond to her hostile feelings. He then replied, "I know what is wrong and I am sorry. I still feel the same way about the ball, and you were wrong in not staying out of my way. But I had no right to speak to you in such a tone of voice." With this her face broke into a smile. She ran over and kissed her father without saying a word.

Family life education in a church setting offers opportunities to teach parents how to handle anger and hostility in their children in such a way as not to provoke them to wrath. The child learns more by identifying himself with the emotional responses of parents than from their verbal teaching.

For Further Reading

ALEXANDER, FRANZ. *Psychosomatic Medicine.* New York: W. W. Norton Company, 1950. Pp. 155-63.

MARCUSSEN, ROBERT M., AND WOLFF, HAROLD G. "A Formulation of the Dynamics of the Migraine Attack," *Psychosomatic Medicine,* 11:251-56, Sept.-Oct. 1949.

MOENCH, LOUIS G. *Headache.* Chicago: The Year Book Publishers, 1947. Pp. 154-97.

TOURAINE, GRACE A., AND DRAPER, GEORGE. "The Migrainous Patient," *Journal of Nervous and Mental Disease,* 80:1-15, July 1934.

WEISS, EDWARD, AND ENGLISH, O. SPURGEON. *Psychosomatic Medicine.* Philadelphia: W. B. Saunders Company, 1957. Pp. 453-58.

WOLFF, HAROLD G. *Headache and Other Head Pain.* New York: Oxford University Press, 1948. Pp. 319-49.

SEVEN

Spiritual Therapy for the Patient with Anxiety and Conversion Reaction

It is well known today how frequently people crowd the offices of the general practitioner and hospitals with physical symptoms for which no organic cause can be determined. As far back as 1943 a standard medical textbook estimated that one-third of the patients who consult a physician are suffering from so-called "functional" problems.[1]

Underneath these functional complaints is often an anxiety pattern. Fever is a common sign that the body is reacting to some biological stress. In similar fashion, the feeling of anxiety may be a danger signal pointing to the threatening existence of unacceptable impulses within the personality. There are a number of ways whereby the person may unconsciously seek to handle this excessive anxiety. It may be experienced as a diffuse apprehensiveness and dread or it may be expressed through depression, compulsive behavior, loss of memory, or the development of physical symptoms.

The chapter on the heart patient discussed in detail how anxiety can become focused upon a particular organ of the body. For example, individuals under emotional strain have walked up a flight of stairs and suddenly become concerned about their rapid heartbeat.

The authors wish to acknowledge their gratitude to Angus Randolph, M.D., Associate Professor of Psychiatry, Bowman Gray School of Medicine and North Carolina Baptist Hospital, for offering valuable suggestions and reading this chapter for medical accuracy.

The concern develops into a fear, which in turn accelerates the heart action. When patients with this type of anxiety enter a hospital they are usually in a state of exhaustion. The anxious state in which the patient has been living may result in loss of sleep and preoccupation with bodily function which increases his apprehensiveness, thus setting up a "vicious cycle."

Anxiety may be expressed through a specific fear. A mother, afraid to be left alone with her two-year-old child, after a period of time developed stomach symptoms which led to her hospitalization. One morning when she was sitting in the kitchen peeling potatoes, she suddenly had the thought, "Suppose I should stick this knife into my child?" The thought was so out of keeping with her character that she immediately wondered, "Why in the world would I have such a thought? I couldn't have thought that." The more she attempted to suppress the idea the more compulsive her thinking became.

There is, however, an additional type of anxiety reaction which is often marked by dramatic physical symptoms, and henceforth seen in the general hospital in sufficient numbers to warrant the awareness of the minister. This disorder is known as "conversion reaction."

In conversion reaction the individual unconsciously "converts" his emotional conflict into a symbolic somatic disturbance.[2] The symptoms typically occur suddenly and in a time of pronounced stress. The sudden onset of the loss of sight or hearing, or a paralysis of an extremity is characteristic of this illness.

The modern development of medical psychology originated in late nineteenth-century studies of conversion reaction known then as "hysteria" or "conversion hysteria." Many of the basic principles of modern psychotherapy grew out of the work of Breuer and Freud with conversion patients. Early interest in the disorder waned but was revived by the frequency of its appearance during the stresses of World Wars I and II. There is generally a feeling that the more dramatic symptoms of the earlier classical cases have become less common today. In their place, however, there may be an increasing frequency of conversion symptoms involving the autonomic nervous system, especially in situations relating to workmen's compensation.[3]

Although any organ or tissue may be the site of conversion,

in general the reactions may be classified as motor, sensory, and autonomic nervous system disturbances. An example of a conversion symptom involving motor disturbance was seen in a fourteen-year-old girl who was brought to the hospital paralyzed from the waist down. Any attempt to change the position of her legs even slightly caused her to cry out in pain. This girl's father had been drinking for several years. One night while drinking he suffered a heart attack and collapsed on the floor. He was a heavy man, but the girl and her mother succeeded in lifting him onto a bed. In the excitement the girl then ran about a hundred yards to the neighbor's house to telephone the doctor and then ran back home. However, in lifting her father the girl strained a muscle in her back and the next day developed functional paralysis from the waist down.

Usually an entire extremity is involved, as in the paralysis of one or both legs or arms. This was commonly seen among soldiers for whom the unconscious incapacitation provided a respectable "answer" to the conflict between the fear of injury and the fear of being called a coward. Neurological examination can usually detect differences between a conversion paralysis and a true organic paralysis. If the conversion illness remains untreated for a long period of time, however, the disuse of the limb may result in muscle atrophy. Conversion paralysis often occurs at or near the location of some pre-existing injury or disease which has subsequently healed.[4]

Another expression of conversion reaction is through sensory disturbances. Typical examples are the sudden onset of blindness or deafness or the loss of feeling in some member of the body.

A seventeen-year-old boy entered the hospital through the neurological service with the chief complaint of loss of feeling in his lower extremities. The only abnormal medical finding was a strained ligament to which the boy had given way completely. This young man was bounced off a tractor while plowing and landed on his back. The next morning when he attempted to get out of bed he felt numbness in his legs and refused to budge until seen by his local physician who referred him to the hospital for evaluation. He had been warned earlier by an uncle that masturbation would "eat the marrow out of his backbone," and his mind reacted to his back pain by saying, "This is it. It finally got me."

The loss of feeling is often experienced as if the person were wearing a glove or stocking on the affected member. This constitutes a difference from the true pattern of nerve distribution. Painful sensations produced in affected areas are transmitted to the central nervous system but are denied consciousness, so that it is possible to stick a pin into an affected limb or to make a sudden noise in psychological deafness without a response from the person who is suffering from conversion reaction.[5]

Occasionally conversion symptoms may be expressed through disturbances of the autonomic nervous system, which is not under conscious control. Hysterical vomiting is an example of a conversion phenomenon involving the autonomic nervous system. The parents of a teen-age girl objected to her dating a certain boy. She continued to see the boy, however, by meeting him at a girl friend's house. The parents discovered what was happening one Sunday night and, when she arrived home about eleven o'clock, created a big scene. The girl was awakened in the middle of the night with nausea and vomiting so severe that she was brought into the hospital where a diagnosis of pernicious vomiting was made.

Medical literature commonly refers to the hysterical personality as being especially prone to conversion reaction, although not all individuals of this personality structure will have conversion reaction. One source describes the hysterical personality as marked by a high degree of suggestibility, an active fantasy life, and an inclination toward vagueness in telling the truth about their medical histories and relationships to other people. Although there appears to be intense affect, oftentimes there is emotional shallowness and instability in interpersonal relationships. This type person tends to become attached to physicians, idealizing them beyond reason, and becoming childishly dependent.[6]

A striking characteristic of the conversion reaction is the calm mental attitude that follows the onset. Such a severe symptom as blindness or paraplegia can apparently leave the conversion patient anxiety-free, whereas organic incapacitation ordinarily heightens concern and anxiety over the condition. This apparent calmness is due to the fact that the symptom is a partial solution, though superficial, to the painful anxiety which existed prior to the conversion.[7]

Conversion reaction may provide the patient with a certain amount of secondary gain which serves to deter him from dealing with the emotional conflict. One study of hysterically paralyzed veterans recommended discharging these patients early, even if it meant sending them home in wheel chairs, rather than allowing them the continued secondary gains in the form of special attention, which hospitalization provided.[8]

The hysterical personality often is attracted by religious symbolism and pageantry. It is interesting that the earliest clinical case records in the English language record the healing of what appears to be a case of conversion reaction. At St. Bartholomew's Hospital in twelfth-century London, "there was a young man, Osberne by name, whose right hand was fixed to his left shoulder. His head, pressed down to the hand, lay immovable. It was impossible to move the hand from the shoulder, nor the head from the hand. When the man approached the altar of the blessed Apostle Bartholomew, with lamenting tears, he humbly besought his mercy. And he desired graciously to be heard. When his limbs were free, he and all those who were present with worthy praise magnified God, who is marvelous in his saints." [9] The appeal of religious symbolism in addition to the frequency with which guilt is associated with anxiety in conversion reaction makes the minister's role on the team strategic in the management of conversion patients.

The following case illustrates the role of religious ministry when conversion reaction is complicated by a strong religious overlay. Miss G, a twenty-one-year-old student, was referred to the hospital from a college infirmary because of pernicious vomiting of three days' duration. On Sunday evening about an hour before she was to have given a devotional talk at a student meeting, she was seized with a sudden and violent attack of vomiting. After several hours she reported to the infirmary and was kept there for the next three days without any improvement. Physical examination in the infirmary and at the hospital failed to uncover any organic basis for her vomiting.

Miss G grew up on a farm and was the oldest of seven children. She described her father as being the disciplinarian in the family and her mother as more indulgent but somewhat emotionally unstable. Although neither of her parents took an active interest in religion, Miss G began attending church in adolescence with other young people in the community. One Sunday night under a strong appeal from a visiting missionary speaker she surrendered her life for missionary service. The church subsequently showered her with attention, making her a Sunday School teacher and youth leader. When the time came for her to go away to college on a scholarship secured by her pastor, the young people of the church showed their interest by giving her a set of luggage.

Miss G's college experience broadened her outlook on life over what it had been at home in a rural community. One day in the middle of her sophomore year during a class in home economics the thought suddenly came to her: "Maybe I would like to teach home economics." She especially liked this teacher. The thought frightened Miss G not only because of having dedicated her life publicly to religious work, but also because she had accepted help as a mission candidate. She tried to put the idea out of her mind, but the thought persisted. Her vomiting was due to her inability to "stomach" the conflict in her life.

This individual came to the attention of the hospital chaplain through a letter from her college pastor who described her as one of the finest Christians girls on the campus. Upon the first visit, the chaplain noted that Miss G was in no apparent emotional distress. She talked freely with him about the religious activities on her campus and in general acted as though everything was "wonderful" except for her nausea. Miss G's physician told the chaplain there were no organic abnormalities and said that he had requested a psychiatric consultation. Neither the chaplain nor the psychiatrist made any progress with this girl in the first two weeks of her hospitalization despite the fact that she was seen every other day by the psychiatrist and on alternate days by the chaplain. During the third week, however, as a result of a probing, frontal approach, the psychiatrist finally succeeded in getting Miss G to admit that things on the inside of her were not as pleasant as she made them appear on the outside.

Aware of this progress, the chaplain on his next visit asked Miss G deliberately and in a directive fashion, "Do you ever have any doubts?" Her response, with a look of astonishment, was a vigorous "superpious" denial. "That's odd," continued the chaplain. "I doubt every day. You mean you never have any doubts at all?" During the remainder of this interview, Miss G came around to admitting there had been times when she had questioned whether or not she wanted to be in full-time religious work. She recalled how this thought had come to her in class and how her vomiting began on Sunday night just prior to a religious meeting.

During the third week her condition began to improve and she was discharged after a hospitalization of four weeks. On several other visits, the chaplain sat by her bed and listened as she explored various vocational opportunities open to her. She finally concluded that after all, she did want to devote her life to religious service. She went on to complete her college and seminary preparation and has been engaged in religious work for the past seven years.

An awareness of the characteristics of conversion reaction can strengthen the effectiveness of the pastoral care of the individuals with this illness.

1. The conversion reaction patient almost invariably displays a calm unruffled exterior after the appearance of the symptom. This was obvious in the case of Miss G who at the end of a half-dozen visits still showed no particular evidences of an emotional or spiritual problem. If the chaplain had not consulted with her physician and psychiatrist, he would have concluded she was well-adjusted with a healthy religious outlook. When the minister learns that the diagnosis does not involve organic impairment, he should avoid reacting to these individuals as if they were hypochondriacs or malingerers. In contrast to the conversion patient, the hypochondriac protests loudly over his symptoms and has a great need to talk about them. The malingerer can be distinguished from the conversion patient by the inconsistency of his symptoms. Malingering paralytics, for example, have been spotted walking about the ward when they thought no

one was looking, but this would never occur in conversion reaction.

2. Conversion reaction is a serious illness despite the fact that the physician can usually remove the symptom with relative ease through suggestion or hypnosis. However, the symptoms are likely to recur in the same or other forms when the individual returns to his stress situation unless the basic conflict is resolved.

This illness is deep-seated and the individual is not consciously aware of the need his symptoms are meeting in his emotional life. For this reason simply telling the person, "There is no organic basis for your illness," is no answer and may serve to frustrate the person all the more. The physician's aim is to help the patient understand the dynamics that produced the condition in the first place. The minister should watch for underlying guilt feelings that might be complicating the anxiety reaction.

No one but professionally trained persons should attempt to deal with conversion reaction. Even the clinically trained minister should not aggressively deal with a conversion patient apart from consultation with and a close working relationship to the physician charged with responsibility in the case.

3. The minister should guard against the mishandling of over-affectionate attachments in the performance of his ministry to the conversion patient. (See the case of Miss J in Chapter Four for a further discussion of this problem.) Conversion patients, because of their high degree of suggestibility, are usually prone to become dependent upon and overaffectionate toward doctors, ministers, and other authority figures. Hysterical persons ordinarily romanticize the majority of their relationships and are therefore likely to do the same thing as they relate to the doctor or minister. The unwise or untrained counselor is apt to react to such positive feelings as if they were expressions of mature emotions. If this occurs it defeats the primary purpose of the therapeutic relationship and fails to allow the individual to understand the persisting emotions dating from childhood.

There is a difference between honest regard and blind crushes or frank sexual attachments which develop suddenly and without due cause. A doctor's words here are appropriate to the minister:

"When one receives an extravagant compliment, one should not jump to the conclusion that it is entirely due to a pleasant manner or helpful skill. There is no harm in taking a piece of it, but one should not eat it all. Surely part of it belongs to someone else and has been offered to the doctor through displacement as a result of causes originating within the patient." [10]

4. The individual with conversion hysteria often attempts an unhealthy use of religion in an effort to control his anxiety. The so-called "superpious" person is an example of what is meant here. This type of individual does not admit to being a member of the human race. The minister can "sense" this when the person's religious experience is not taking into account the raw facts of human nature and the impartiality of natural law. It is easy to be blinded by the hysterical person's religious fervor to the extent that one fails to see the possibility of the individual's religious experience being a cover-up mechanism dissociated from reality. Rather than support an unrealistic outlook a better approach is for the minister to insist gently but firmly upon a constant facing of all the facts in the situation. This, together with his willingness to listen to the individual verbalize his anxieties, can often bring about a healthier religious outlook.

5. The anxious and hysterically inclined person often falls prey to unscrupulous religious quacks because of his responsiveness to emotional stimulation.

In the same way that the doctor seeks to guard cancer patients from exploitation by cancer quacks, the minister may guard emotionally susceptible persons through an adequate program of education. He can stress the fact that the Bible does not set scientific knowledge over against religious faith. After all, God can be at work through the various instrumentalities of the healing team whether it is the surgeon's knife or the prayer of faith.

For Further Reading

BROWN, WILLIAM, AND PISETSKY, JOSEPH. "Sociopsychologic Factors in Hyssterical Paraplegia," *Journal of Nervous and Mental Disease,* 119:283-98, April 1954.

CHODOFF, P., AND LYONS, H. "Hysteria, the Hysterical Personality, and Hysterical Conversion," *American Journal of Psychiatry,* 114:734-40, Feb. 1958.

ENGLISH, O. SPURGEON, AND FINCH, STUART M. *Introduction to Psychiatry.* New York: W. W. Norton and Company, 1954. Pp. 139-79.

LIGHTBURN, JOHN L., CATTELL, RICHARD B., AND STEVENSON, WILLIAM F. "Differential Diagnosis of Conversion Reaction in a General Hospital," *Postgraduate Medicine,* 23:140-47, Feb. 1958.

MAY, ROLLO. *The Meaning of Anxiety.* New York: The Ronald Press Company, 1950.

OATES, WAYNE E. *Anxiety in Christian Experience.* Philadelphia: The Westminster Press, 1955.

WEISS, EDWARD, AND ENGLISH, O. SPURGEON. *Psychosomatic Medicine.* Philadelphia: W. B. Saunders Company, 1957. Pp. 38-46.

EIGHT *Spiritual Therapy for the Surgical Patient*

To place one's life literally in the hands of a surgeon, no matter how skilled he might be, is a sobering experience. Even in relatively simple surgical procedures, the patient normally feels some degree of apprehensiveness and fear. Radical surgery can disturb the total psychic equilibrium, resulting in such severe emotional reactions as the loss of the will to live or chronic invalidism. One psychiatrist has observed that anesthesia, cutting of the body, and alteration of the body parts can in extreme cases precipitate a psychosis.[1] The pastor who attempts to render an adequate ministry to surgical patients needs to be aware of some of the emotional implications of surgery.

The way in which a person learns of his need for surgery affects his emotional responses. To come into the hospital on a medical service and have the doctor announce unexpectedly the need for a critical operation can be a shocking experience. To be told of an immediate need for an operation is far different than to be advised to "go home and when you get in good physical shape come in this fall and we will take care of that gall bladder." Or, in another situation, the individual may be enduring such severe pain as to welcome

The authors are indebted to Howard Bradshaw, M.D., Professor of Surgery, Bowman Gray School of Medicine and North Carolina Baptist Hospital, for contributing to this chapter and reading the whole for medical accuracy.

an operation. Again, there are a few individuals who seem to enjoy being cut on to the point of attempting to badger the surgeon into performing an operation that may not really be necessary.

It is important to know how the individual is responding emotionally to the news of his impending operation. The normal anxieties and fears of the surgical patient take many forms.

In some instances anxiety over an economic factor may be a first concern of the patient. Questions that may plague the patient at a time like this have to do with absence from the family in the case of a mother, absence from work in the case of a father, length of the interruption of employment, implications of the surgery for future employment, and the cost of the operation itself. In spite of hospitalization insurance, social security, and unemployment compensation, there are still a number of individuals who postpone or refuse needed surgery because of finances. On more than one occasion in a medical center where denominational funds were available the chaplain has had the privilege of persuading individuals who were going home and refusing elective surgery because of a lack of funds to accept the help available to them.

Fear may arise from ignorance of various procedures used in preparing the patient for surgery. Occasionally a patient may interpret the signing of the necessary permission for the operation as an indication that his situation is critical. Explaining that this is simply a hospital routine will often dispel this apprehension.

Fear and anxiety tend to increase during a waiting period which may be required while laboratory specimens are being evaluated. This is especially true where cancer is suspected. Everyone has heard of operations where it was not possible to remove all of the cancerous tissue.

Some surgical procedures necessarily demand drastic readjustments in one's way of life. Dread of the consequences may exceed fear of the operation itself. A colostomy patient, for example, would gladly undergo the operation if by doing so he could escape a condition that will exist for the remainder of his life.

A very frequent source of fear has to do with anesthesia. Concern over the discomfort of breathing the anesthetic can be alleviated by the explanation that sedation is often given before the patient is taken to the operating room. In most hospitals, the anesthesiologist will give this explanation in a visit to the patient prior to surgery. However, a more real fear of anesthesia stems from the patient's reluctance to relinquish conscious control of his life. There are few other situations where the person becomes as utterly helpless and at the mercy of the skill of fallible human beings. The most common questions after the experience is over are, "How did I act? What did I say?"

Few patients enter surgery without at least a fleeting thought of the possibility of death. In extreme cases where the patient lacks a desire to live or has a fixed conviction that he is going to die the surgeon will refuse to operate unless death is impending. The reason for this is that there have been occasions where despite mechanically successful surgery, the patient died. One surgeon in discussing the pitfalls in preoperative and postoperative care says, "We have all seen a masterpiece of surgery fail, only because the patient had lost all desire to live." [2]

While normal fears prior to an operation are important, the emotional consequences of surgery can be even more serious. Surgery can disrupt a long-standing personality pattern. This was anticipated by a twenty-seven-year-old man who refused to allow the amputation of a leg because as he said, "My whole life has been built around my leg." Since the age of ten when his leg was injured he had had intermittent infection and constant trouble. His mother had cared for him continuously, and at the time surgery was advised she was hovering over him in the hospital room as if he were still ten years old.

For some patients surgery seems to furnish a means of atoning for underlying guilt. This person unconsciously believes that literally "without the shedding of blood there is no remission of sins." The feeling that the operation is a punishment sent by God meets an emotional need. In a euphoric state one patient said, two days after an operation, "I know God brought this upon me, but for some reason I feel much better." The chaplain could not find any other logical interpretation to explain the patient's elation but that satisfaction was derived from the ordeal. Surgeons are quite suspicious of the person who has a history of various and frequent operations.[3]

Major surgery makes the patient physically dependent upon others for feeding, eliminating, bathing, and dressing. From a psychological standpoint the adult is reduced to an infantile level of helplessness, from which he gradually recuperates toward independence once more. The last stages of convalescence bear a striking resemblance to adolescence. The adolescent talks big, as though he doesn't want anybody to help him make a decision, when all the time, deep down, he is very shaky in trusting his own judgment. He is really whistling in the dark. The convalescent who is recuperating from major surgery is no longer fighting for his life. With his body free from pain, in his mind he is thinking big about "getting going again," but when he steps off the bed, his knees buckle under him. Passing through this experience tends to awaken any dependency needs that may exist in the personality. This can create problems for medical and nursing personnel and for the family who may find the patient becoming extremely demanding if he has enjoyed being dependent. On the other hand, if dependence is repulsive to him, the patient may strike out at those around him and in some instances become very cantankerous.

Reactive depression may follow drastic surgery. Anytime there is an alteration of the body image one's self-concept is likely to be affected. How vitally the surgery will affect the personality is largely dependent upon the significance of the affected organ for the body image. The appendix, for example, is not nearly so important to the body image as an arm or leg. One young man at home on furlough accidentally shot himself while hunting. The time which elapsed between the accident and his arrival at the hospital necessitated the removal of his leg. For five days he did not speak to a doctor, nurse, or anyone else and remained in an almost stuporous depression. The chaplain visited him daily and observed his gradual response to the skilled attention given to him by the entire medical staff, who helped him eventually face up to his rehabilitation problem.

The body image is more deeply affected by the removal of reproductive organs than by any other type of drastic surgery. This type of surgery threatens the individual's manhood or womanhood. In one study of four hundred patients who had hysterectomy operations Lindemann found that 40 per cent of them became depressed during the first postoperative year.[4] Operations affecting reproductive organs are often interpreted as loss of sexual ability even when they do not actually cause sterility.[5]

Because the surgeon confronts the patient daily, he must of necessity develop a philosophy toward his ministry, a knowledge of which can benefit the pastor who must often deal with the same problems. In the following paragraphs Howard Bradshaw summarizes from his experience a surgeon's awareness of, and response to, his patient's anxieties:

"The emotional reaction of a patient to a surgical experience reflects in great measure the kind of life he has previously led. A patient who has been honest and considerate with his family and his fellow man and who has led a Christian existence, is rarely overly disturbed by contemplating the ordeals of anesthesia and surgery. Whatever reaction a patient may have can be greatly influenced by his contacts with the surgeon and other hospital personnel. If everyone who contacts the patient does so with a feeling of sympathy, understanding and helpfulness, he cannot help but be calmed and assured to some extent.

"We all fear the unknown. The two questions foremost in the mind of a patient are, 'How much will all this cost me, and what will be my chance for a normal healthy existence after this is over?' The first question should be answered quite accurately by a friendly interview with the business manager or some other financial officer of the hospital. This practice is growing in hospitals but was almost unheard of except in private clinics until fairly recently.

"The other question should be clarified by the operating surgeon. He should sit down with the patient and explain what he thinks should be done and why. He should explain whether an operation is more or less risky. This can be done in the course of the conversation without frightening the patient too much. If an operation carries considerable risk with it, certainly the patient and his family have a right to know it. Who knows what thoughts cross a man's mind when he is contemplating the possibility of death? He might want to change his will or have a long session with his minister or settle important business affairs. Furthermore, he should be told about postoperative pain and its relief, how long he should be in the hospital and how long his convalescence will require. In other words a patient who has been properly prepared for operation makes an understanding, well-adjusted patient in the postoperative and convalescent periods." [6]

The basic problems faced to some degree by all surgical patients, from fear of the operation all the way to rehabilitation, are magnified in the amputee. Mr. D, a forty-six-year-old carnival worker, was run over by a trailer truck and suffered the injury of both legs, one of which required amputation. His life savings had been wiped out by medical expenses which followed. Six years later while the carnival was in town he came to the emergency room of the hospital to get something for pain, but was admitted for possible amputation of his remaining leg.

Mr. D, the youngest of three children, lost his father when he was too young to remember. He lived with his grandmother until he was sixteen years old at which time he began working with a carnival. In conversations with the chaplain he would often say, "I have never felt like I belonged to anyone." He seemed to have no relationship with his brother or sister. The patient stated, "They are too busy to care about me. One has three children and the other has seven." On several occasions he said, "When you are in my business you don't have time to put roots down anywhere. I am a man without a country."

When Mr. D first entered the hospital he looked upon God as a severe disciplinarian as evidenced by such remarks as, "If it were not God's will I would not have been run over. If it is God's will I will die on the operating table. If not, I won't. Every person in this hospital is being punished by God for his sins. What is to be will be and we can't help it."

The doctors felt that his leg should be amputated but hesitated to operate until they could be assured that he could be rehabilitated with artificial legs. The state vocational rehabilitation service studied his case but because he was a nonresident could not give assistance, which caused a postponement of the date set for his surgery. The intensity of Mr. D's disappointment following this news was seen in his statement to the chaplain: "When the doctor told me he could not get artificial legs for me I started planning to kill myself. You may think I didn't mean it, but I had rather be dead than face life with nothing to look forward to but pain with this leg."

On the strength of the chaplain's promise to locate some means of buying artificial limbs for Mr. D, the operation was rescheduled and successfully performed. The patient was in and out of a depression until he was finally convinced that he would get the legs. "Chaplain, I guess I have never been able to trust anyone," commented Mr. D. "I did not believe you were really going to help me until I awoke after surgery and reached for that bad leg and it was gone. Even then I was more scared than ever because I started thinking what would happen to me if you did not get the legs and I had to leave the hospital with no legs at all. I do not think I started trusting you deep down until that man came and took my measurements. After that I just leaned back and was happy for the first time in my life. Boy, I really found out what Christian love is."

By this time Mr. D's stay in the hospital had given him some sense of belonging. This was reflected in a softening of his religious attitudes when he said, "Maybe God does care what happens to me."

After his discharge from the hospital Mr. D lived at the Salvation Army Shelter and arrangements were made for him to come back and forth to the rehabilitation clinic at the hospital. The chaplain secured the artificial legs by calling local ministers and church organizations. The manufacturer agreed to furnish the limbs at a discount. The story got into the newspaper during this time, and a number of other individuals made contributions. A Ringling Brothers performer sent in twenty-five dollars. Mr. D said, "Chaplain, I have had people stop while I was sitting in front of the Salvation Army Shelter and tell me they were praying for me. They would then hand me some money and simply say, 'I saw your picture in the paper and I want to have a part in getting your legs.' One woman called me long distance and talked fifteen minutes. She said she had been in a wheelchair for a long time and knew how I felt and encouraged me to keep fighting. You know, for the first time in my life I feel I have some friends that really care for me."

The specific ministry to this patient is obvious. As a "man without a country," he basically needed the warmth of Christian love in order to grow emotionally and spiritually. This he received from the doctors, nurses, and the entire hospital team. But the business of a hospital is to translate religious concern into intelligently practical forms of help. Concern for his basic need was made tangible through charitable surgery and the securing of his artificial limbs. The power of Christian love almost literally rebuilt this man physically and spiritually, and in the process radically changed his attitude toward his fellow man and God.

There are problems peculiar to the amputee in addition to those faced by all surgical patients. As soon as he learns that amputation of a limb is necessary, the patient begins a process of self-evaluation which extends throughout every area of his life. Such questions as "Why did my religion not protect me from this?" "How am I going to face my family and friends?" "What will happen to my job and educational plans?" "Will I be able to get married and raise a family?" indicate how the amputee begins to grapple with readjustment even before the operation. The patient with a healthy religious outlook and strong personality characteristics who is well established socially, economically, and vocationally is less likely to become extremely dependent upon the hospital team than the patient with weak personality traits, indefinite family ties, and little ambition educationally and vocationally. Adequate preparation before the operation will facilitate the patient's emotional adjustment during rehabilitation.

Regardless of the strength of the personality of the amputee, he is likely to have bouts of depression during the course of his hospitalization. As mentioned earlier in this chapter his depression is a reaction to the loss of body parts, which the amputee experiences as partial death. According to Meyer, amputation may therefore "be accompanied by affects akin to mourning." [7] In addition to injury to the self-esteem which results from amputation, the grief process tends to revive or reinforce psychic experiences pertaining to significant persons in the patient's life.

Like the bereaved person, the amputee first tends to deny the reality of his loss. Such statements as "You don't need two legs except for swimming," "You see more when you walk slowly," signify attempts at denial, just as mild euphoria denies anxiety over the loss.[8] The person may for a time avoid looking at the stump. Denial may constitute a double-edged weapon, at times giving the patient merciful protection, and at other times causing him to postpone medical care and in some cases sweeping the person into a psychosis.[9]

In contrast to denial, some patients in the early stages react with defiance and declare, "This will never get me down." On the other hand, there are those who become very aggressive and feel society has treated them unfairly, and take out their feelings on those who are trying to help. Fortunately, the larger number of amputees accept and become resigned to the fact of amputation and search for compensatory factors to balance their loss.[10]

Most adult amputees experience "phantom limb" sensations at some time following surgery. The patient feels as though his limb were still "there" when in fact it is not. The limb is supposed to assume the posture last remembered by the person. An accidental amputation results in a longer lasting phantom than a planned one which follows psychological preparation. The phantoms of upper extremities are usually stronger and more enduring than those of lower extremities since the hand transmits more sensations to the brain than any other part of the body. In the folklore of many countries beliefs exist that the amputated limb should be disposed of in a known, safe place so that later all of the body can be buried together. Severe chronic phantom pain often becomes a factor in alcoholism and drug addiction.[11]

Self-pity, in all of its insidious forms, should be recognized as probably one of the most destructive emotions the amputee experiences and should be fought vigorously by the entire healing team.[12] Self-pity tends to be less severe where the patient is among other patients with similar problems such as occurs in military or veterans hospitals.

Because of the wide variety of surgical procedures and the uniqueness of each patient's response, the pastor confronts many different problems in ministering to surgical patients. Nevertheless, there are certain basic suggestions that should prove helpful.

1. In the preoperative stage the pastor's ministry is largely one of going alongside, giving comfort and encouragement to the patient. Pastoral care of the patient who is steeling himself for the ordeal of surgery is somewhat like that rendered by the chaplain to soldiers on the eve of battle. Probably the best resource for alleviating fear is that of listening to the apprehensions of the patient as he brings them out into the open and philosophizes about his life. When a friendly relationship has been established the pastor can aid the individual to bring his feelings out into the open by asking, "How do you feel about the coming operation?" Most patients welcome the opportunity to express themselves.

When the patient is not well-acquainted with his surgeon and may be having a first operation, to encourage his faith in the doctor may dispel some of his apprehensions. The pastor may have already visited other patients of this surgeon and be able sincerely to say, "You certainly have a capable doctor. I have known him for several years and have a great deal of confidence in his skill as a surgeon."

2. The pastor should be alert for any signs of guilt or desire for confession during a visit to the preoperative patient. Clinical experience indicates that one of the most significant phases of the preoperative ministry has to do with strengthening the individual's will to live. The effective use of religious resources can often generate a poise which conditions the total organism. As one surgeon has said, "Adequate help by the clergy and social service in the preoperative period is often rewarded by a grateful, relaxed, co-operative patient who has a benign, uneventful postoperative course." [13]

One evening about ten-thirty a chaplain was called to the hospital to see a lady who was scheduled for surgery the next morning. According to the nurse the patient had received sedatives, but was still crying and said that she did not care whether she lived or died.

Upon entering the room, immediately after the introduction the patient said, "Chaplain, I'm glad you're here. I want you to pray for me." The chaplain responded, "I will be glad to pray with you, but let's get a little better acquainted so that I can pray more intelligently."

Very shortly thereafter the patient made the following confession. She related how she had been in a car wreck three months earlier, necessitating this operation which she now interpreted as God's punishment upon her for sin. She was talking about the fact that her second child was not by her husband. The chaplain read to her Jesus' teachings about adultery and led her through an experience of forgiveness. She went through the operation successfully and showed no further signs of apprehensiveness. The experience of forgiveness through the ministry of confession is often of real value in strengthening the patient's will to live.

Fear of death also can intensify the individual's need to make things right with God and his fellow man before going to the operating room. There have been times when patients stubbornly insisted on seeing the chaplain and refused to be carried to the operating room until they did.

3. The pastor must necessarily watch the timing of his visits to surgical patients. The afternoon or evening prior to surgery is the ideal time for a preoperative visit. Any beneficial effects of the pastor's visit will thus be carried through the night and will help to prepare the patient emotionally and spiritually for the operation. Access to the patient on the morning of surgery is difficult due to preoperative medication.

During surgery and immediately thereafter the pastor should focus his attention upon the family. If the operation is critical, the family will also be battling with fear and anxiety and will deeply appreciate the support they derive from the pastor's presence during the sometimes long hours that the family must wait. The pastor helps the family during this time not so much by what he says as by his presence.

For several days after a major operation, the pastor should keep his visits brief. Often the patient is uncomfortable, receiving intravenous fluids, and may be nauseated and is in no condition to carry on a sustained conversation. Like the ministry to the family, pastoral care of the patient at this time is more a relationship of going alongside offering strength and encouragement through his presence. In the later stages of convalescence the patient becomes more concerned about future adjustments and the minister can then use the religious resources of counseling with the individual.

4. Operations that affect the body image and self-esteem require closer attention than less drastic types of surgery. The depression that tends to follow radical surgery is related to the unconscious bereavement for the lost member of the body or over the deformity which has taken place. As in his ministry to the bereaved, the pastor should let the individual talk about his loss, which will enable him to accept the reality of the situation in a healthy manner.

The pastor may secure the patient's permission to invite someone who has had a similar experience to visit with the patient. He can suggest this by saying, "I have a friend who has faced the same thing confronting you." The chaplain of one hospital keeps on file a list of people who have adjusted to artificial limbs, blindness, colostomies, and similar handicaps who have volunteered their services anytime they are notified.

5. A majority of all persons who have major surgery can be rehabilitated. The U. S. Naval Hospital, Oakland, California, treated over seven thousand amputees during an eleven-year period and found in its experience that 94 per cent of amputees could be successfully rehabilitated.[14] Many amputees return to the same or similar types of work and some become financially better off. So often there is no attempt to rehabilitate the elderly person who has an amputation due to a failure in blood circulation, yet a study of forty-nine elderly double above-the-knee amputees showed that the survival rate to five years after surgery was quite adequate to justify the rehabilitation efforts.[15]

In almost every community there are individuals who are a burden to themselves and to their families because no one has taken the trouble to inform them of the available sources of help and encourage them to make the effort. In one community a ladies' auxiliary assumed responsibility for transporting a helpless elderly man to a rehabilitation clinic once a week for three months with the result that he became able to dress and care for himself once again.

The cost of lengthy hospitalization, prosthetic appliances, and rehabilitation often discourages the family from seeking medical help and a majority need outside financial assistance, particularly elderly people. Seldom does the amputee or his family apply directly to an agency for help; hence, the pastor can render strategic service by referring these people to appropriate agencies. (A list of national agencies interested in rehabilitation is given at the end of this chapter.)

6. Self-pity, at one time or another, tends to plague the person who has undergone major surgery. The family may at times unwittingly reinforce this self-pity by attempting to do for the patient things he needs to be learning to do for himself. In his own contacts the pastor can avoid doing anything which tends to undercut the person's confidence in himself and should share this idea with the family when possible.

What the pastor communicates through his own emotional attitude can hinder or help the individual's adjustment. What has been said of the psychiatrist by Meyer applies equally to the pastor, namely, that he "is expected to possess that more-than-a-nodding acquaintance with his own emotional reactions which will help insure for the sick patient warmth without heat, light without fire, and air without drafts." [16]

NATIONAL AGENCIES FOR REHABILITATION

American Board for Certification of the Prosthetic and Orthopedic Appliance Industry, Inc., Suite 130, 919 Eighteenth Street, Washington 6, D.C. This Board appraises (1) individual technicians to make certain that they are qualified to fit and fabricate the various types of artificial limbs and braces and (2) facilities to make certain that claims of cleanliness, safety, and competence are borne out in day-to-day practice. A Registry of Certified Facilities is available upon request.

American National Red Cross, Seventeenth and D Streets, N.W., Washington 6, D.C. Through its thirty-six hundred chapters it sponsors home nursing care training and referral service.

Goodwill Industries of America, Inc., 1913 N Street, N.W., Washington 6, D.C. Through one hundred twenty-four local organizations it encourages the establishment and development in various centers of Goodwill Industries for the employment and the religious, cultural, and educational welfare of the handicapped.

Institute for the Crippled and Disabled, 400 First Avenue, New York 10, N. Y., provides a comprehensive, out-patient program of rehabilitation services including medical care, vocational evaluation, and training and social adjustment services for persons whose disabilities are primarily physical and emotional. Referrals for admission should be addressed to the Registrar.

National Rehabilitation Association, 1025 Vermont Avenue, N.W., Washington 5, D.C. Promotes programs for the rehabilitation of mentally and physically handicapped persons.

National Society for Crippled Children and Adults, 2023 W. Ogden Avenue, Chicago 12, Illinois. Through its two thousand state and local units it maintains a staff of professional consultants for the handicapped; also maintains a national professional registry and employment service; issues literature and periodicals.

Office of Vocational Rehabilitation, Washington 25, D.C., provides vocational rehabilitation for physically and mentally handicapped civilians. The program provides physical examination, necessary medical, surgical, psychiatric, and hospital treatment, artificial limbs, hearing aids, as well as individual counseling and vocational training, job placement and post-placement follow-up.

Rehabilitation Commission, The American Legion, 1608 K Street, N.W., Washington 6, D.C., through more than eighteen thousand local posts offers service to veterans.

Veterans Administration, Washington 25, D.C., administers laws relating to benefits provided for former members of the military and naval forces; also administers the government life insurance of veterans and those in active military services. Operates one hundred seventy hospitals and ninety-four out-patient clinics.

124

For Further Reading

CHIVERS, NORMAN, AND DORPAT, THEODORE L. "Emotional Reactions to Surgical Procedures," *GP,* 17:108-11, May 1958.

DEUTSCH, HELENE. "Some Psychoanalytic Observations in Surgery," *Psychosomatic Medicine,* 4:105-15, Jan. 1942.

DRELLICH, MARVIN G., AND BIEBER, IRVING. "The Psychologic Importance of the Uterus and Its Functions," *Journal of Nervous and Mental Disease,* 126:322-36, April 1958.

KELHAM, R. L. "Some Thoughts on Mental Effects of Amputation," *British Medical Journal,* 1:34, Feb. 8, 1958.

KESSLER, H. H. "Psychological Preparation of the Amputee," *Industrial Medicine and Surgery.* 20:107-8, March 1951.

MENNINGER, KARL A. "Polysurgery and Polysurgical Addiction," *Psychoanalytic Quarterly,* 3:173, 1934.

MEYER, BERNARD C. "Some Psychiatric Aspects of Surgical Practice," *Psychosomatic Medicine,* 20:203-14, May-June 1958.

WEISS, EDWARD, AND ENGLISH, O. SPURGEON. *Psychosomatic Medicine.* Philadelphia: W. B. Saunders Company, 1957. Pp. 495-503.

YOUNG, RICHARD K. *The Pastor's Hospital Ministry.* Nashville: Broadman Press, 1954. Pp. 94-106.

NINE   *Spiritual Therapy at the Birth of Children*

The obstetrical floor of a hospital probably witnesses more extremes both of joy and of sorrow than any other section of the institution. The act of childbirth brings to focus months of hopeful planning sometimes mingled with anxious dread. If the parents want the child and the birth is normal the occasion is one of sublime joy and a spiritual experience. If, on the other hand, the child is unwelcome or in some way malformed the experience may bring tragic suffering. A majority of all childbirths today take place in a hospital, and it is here that the minister frequently has his first visit with new parents. Although not normally a disease process, childbirth is a significant crisis in the family life and as such offers important opportunities for pastoral care.

Because of the risk of infection, the patient's need for rest, and various nursing routines, the obstetrical unit is highly regimented. Babies must be brought to the mothers for feeding at various times around the clock, the mother may be receiving special treatments such as sitz baths and heat lamps. These routines often make the minister's access to the maternity patient difficult.

In addition to the complexity of work schedules on the ob-

The authors wish to acknowledge their gratitude to Frank Lock, M.D., Professor of Obstetrics and Gynecology, Bowman Gray School of Medicine and North Carolina Baptist Hospital, for contributing to this chapter and reading the whole for medical accuracy.

stetrical unit, the pastor needs to understand something of the normal emotional reactions to childbirth. The mother of a newborn baby is tired, uncomfortable from her stitches, and may have after-pains. Her first concern immediately following delivery is "Is the baby normal?" Her suspicions and anxieties will be allayed completely only when she has seen the baby for herself.

Many thoughts may be passing through the mother's mind during the next two or three days. The baby may not be the sex she "ordered" and certainly is not as pretty as she wants to think he is. After nine months of conditioned thinking, there may be a few days before she begins to think automatically in terms of the child's being here. She may be concerned over whether she wants to or will be able to nurse her baby. As she ponders going home her thoughts may wander toward the inescapable changes which this baby will bring into her pattern of life.

By the time the mother forgets about the pain and the baby becomes a reality she may experience attacks of the blues, a perfectly normal reaction. Release from tension and fears usually manifests itself in a tendency to weep sometime between the third and the fifth day following delivery. Since she usually finds no specific reason for the crying, the mother may say, "I do not know why I'm crying. Everything is just wonderful. But I can't help it." The reaction can be agitated by too many visitors asking about all the "gory details."

The significance of the experience of childbirth is discussed in detail in such standard textbooks on the family as the one by Willard Waller and Reuben Hill referred to at the end of this chapter. Parenthood calls for drastic revisions in one's self-concept and family role. The man begins to think of himself as a father as well as a husband. The woman begins to see herself as a mother and no longer as simply a bride or wife. Meeting this responsibility is the greatest test of the parents' maturity up to this time in their lives.

The first arrival also tends to compel a readjustment of the couple to their larger community. A wife may face the interruption of employment outside the home and the restriction of her social contacts. She may either take this in stride with a sense of relief, or be impatient to return to her job.

The time of the first child's arrival in relation to the date of the marriage may be an important factor in the marital adjustment of the parents. If the child comes during the first year of marriage the husband may not have had time to adjust to his wife's characteristic personality before he encountered the personality of a pregnant woman. Likewise the wife may not have had time to adjust to the husband's peculiarities before the added problems of pregnancy. Furthermore, the couple's economic plans may be affected. Consequently there may be unresolved tensions in the marital relationship.

A mother giving birth to a second child has familiarity with the birth procedure and various routines. She may have less anxiety over the childbirth experience but added worries over the problems created by her absence from home. If the birth of the second child is unplanned and happened too close to the arrival of the first child, then the mother has two babies on her hands at the same time. She may have built up unconscious resentment or may have adjusted to making the most of the situation by the time of her delivery.

A late child coming during the menopause, after the mother had concluded that her childbearing phase was past, can create an entirely new set of problems and calls for a radical change in the couple's pattern of living. Not only are the parents themselves unprepared for the child, but their older children and the community at large may view this circumstance with a tinge of social disapproval. A rural community humorously referred to one such couple as "Abraham and Sarah."

Although resentment of pregnancy is occasionally seen in the early phases of prenatal care, obstetricians note that it tends to diminish with time. Resentment and confusion disappear when the family comes to accept the new member and to plan his or her place in the present and the future. Acceptance often begins by the time of the second contact with the doctor and usually some enthusiasm by the third or fourth visit. No normal person can continue to reject a helpless bonafide member of his family.[1]

Pastoral care at the birth of children is one of the most strategic opportunities the minister has to make Christianity an integral part of family life. The thrust of having a part in the creation of a new life does more to bring to the surface the best in a person than any other life situation. Birth represents the only unfinished part of God's creative process. It is a profound and awesome experience to realize that one is having a part with God in the act of creation. Assuming responsibility for the young until they can stand alone even takes precedence over the drive for self-preservation. Recognizing the religious potentialities inherent in the parent-child relationship, the church has for centuries provided various ministries at the birth of a child. Whether or not childbirth has genuine religious significance and becomes a maturing Christian experience is influenced to a large degree by the quality of pastoral care provided at this time.

The following suggestions have proven helpful in ministering to patients on the obstetrical unit of the hospital:

1. Always check with the head nurse before making any visit on the obstetrical unit. This will avoid embarrassing the patient. She may be receiving treatment and has no way of knowing who is knocking on her door. One minister who went directly to the room found a patient experiencing labor pains prior to being moved into the labor room. The patient bitterly resented this blunder.

2. Know the facts before the first visit to the new mother. One physician has said, "No doctor in his right mind who either delivers or is called to see a newly born baby will discuss that baby with the mother until he has made a careful examination." [2] Likewise, no minister should enter the room of a mother without accurate information about the newborn child. The head nurse or a member of the family will be able to tell the minister of anything out of the ordinary. If there has been a stillbirth or the child is malformed in any way, his approach will be more tactful if he can say, "I'm sorry to hear what happened," rather than having to elicit this information from the patient. In a four-bed ward a minister talked to three of the women about their babies, then turned to the fourth and asked, "And what was yours?" Her child had been born dead the previous day.

3. Time your visits in keeping with the obstetrical unit's rou-

tine. Visitors are excluded from rooms and halls while infants are being carried back and forth from the nursery for feedings. This occasions some restriction in the hours available to the minister for visitation. Nevertheless, since the minister is the only person charged specifically with a spiritual ministry to the patient, he should not be discouraged by these routines to the point that he fails to render meaningful pastoral care.

4. Keep visits with a new mother brief, except under unusual circumstances. The patient has passed through an exhausting physical and emotional experience and needs rest. One of the most frequent remarks made by obstetrical patients is, "It's really wonderful to get a chance to be waited on and everybody says I had better rest while I can!" If pain is present, it is often localized in a region of the body not referred to in public. Long visits on the day when the patient is experiencing the most discomfort will not strengthen a relationship.

5. Follow the mother's feelings. Do not enter the room displaying exuberant goodwill, but wait for the patient to set the tone of the visit by her own mood. She may be in the clouds or she may be in the valley, either of which is perfectly normal following childbirth.

6. Do not project your own feelings about parenthood upon the mother. Because of the teachings of the church on family life and the fact that most ministers are parents, there is a strong tendency for the pastor to read his own ideals and adjustments into a visit with a new mother. The minister may not know what it is to be in an iron lung but the chances are that he has experienced parenthood. The ideals of the church notwithstanding, more unwanted children are born into this world than we like to admit. To project into the situation an unsolicited statement such as, "I know you are happy about the coming of this child," is to miss the point completely if you are talking to the mother of an unwanted baby.

7. Watch for any opportunities to counsel with the mother of the newborn. Extensive counseling during hospitalization is not possible because of the brevity of her stay and her condition immediately following delivery. Nevertheless, the very nature of the

experience itself tends to bring to the surface any friction in the marriage, apprehensiveness over assuming the role of a mother, and other issues which the mother knows will arise as soon as she reaches home.

There are subtle teaching opportunities which arise if the pastor is aware of the emotional forces at work in the family unit. Helping persons without their knowledge that they are being helped is probably the highest and finest form of counseling. For example, the mother often refers to the other children at home. The pastor may ask how the two children at home feel about the new baby. This can lead naturally to a discussion of sibling rivalry. The mother recognizes jealousy between the children but may not understand the dynamics involved or how to handle it. The pastor can then, through an illustration, share basic knowledge of personality development in a natural setting.

8. Pray briefly and specifically when offering prayer with the new mother. Avoid too much pious sentimentality such as thanking God for the "little cherub" that has come into the family. The prayer should voice gratitude to God for sustaining the mother and for the normality of the child and should invoke divine guidance for the parental care of the child. The words of Hannah: "For this child I prayed" (I Sam. 1:27), and of Manoah: "How shall we order the child, and how shall we do unto him?" (Judg. 13:12), are appropriate.

9. Use literature to supplement pastoral care of the new parent. It is just as appropriate to loan or give a carefully selected book or other literature to the mother with a first child as it is to present a book to a wedding couple. In some denominational hospitals the chaplains make it a practice to present all the mothers with a white New Testament with the name of the child inscribed on it. Some churches give a subscription to their denominational family magazine at this time. The pastor can loan books like D. W. Winnicott's *Mother and Child, A Primer of First Relationships,* or he may present gift copies of such books as Helen Good Brenneman's *Meditations for the New Mother,* or Frances P. Reid's *None So Small.* There are a number of excellent pamphlets also available at modest

cost. For example, James L. Hymes, *Enjoy Your Child—Ages 1, 2, and 3* (Public Affairs Pamphlet, number 141), or the one put out by the U. S. Children's Bureau, *Infant Care,* which is available from most health departments or the Government Printing Office. The American Medical Association's *Calling All Parents,* is another good pamphlet for this purpose. (Publication data for this material is given at the end of the chapter.)

The birth of a stillborn child, a malformed child, or a child born out of wedlock will intensify the pastoral care of the parents.

In the case of stillbirth the pastor is confronted with a decisive bereavement situation affecting both parents. In this type of bereavement all of the energy and hopes invested during the period of pregnancy have come to nought. The grief can be intensified and complicated by such factors as the absence of other children, the length of time the parents have wanted a child, and whether or not other children are possible. The pastor's first contact with the bereaved mother in the hospital can help her begin her grief reaction in a healthy manner. The first stages of bereavement are discussed in Chapter Eleven.

"Will the child be normal?" is one of the universal fears among prospective parents. This is voiced time and time again in such statements as "It doesn't make any difference which sex the baby is as long as he is normal." The chance that a child will be born with some sort of congenital anomaly is approximately one out of every two hundred births.[3] When an abnormal child is born, Park White says, "In view of the marvelous advances in plastic surgery, we may divide congenital malformations into those about which something definite can be done with every hope of success; those about which something can and should be done, the success of which is doubtful; and those about which, in all honesty, nothing can or should be done save only adjustment, 'learning to live with it.' "[4] The first, or readily reparable group, according to White, includes such conditions as harelip, cleft palate, certain types of birthmarks, clubfeet, and most congenital hernias. Among the more serious and possibly reparable defects are exstrophy of the bladder, congenital cataract, certain operable heart abnormalities, and various types of intestinal obstructions. Finally there are the heart-rending cases where the child is irremediably malformed or "retarded." This group includes mongolism, cerebral palsy, blindness, and inoperable heart conditions.

A blind child with cleft palate and grotesquely deformed limbs was born to Mrs. C. As soon as she recovered from the anesthesia she asked about her baby and was told the truth by her doctor. She became hysterical and the chaplain was called to talk with Mrs. C, but was never really able to get her attention because of her emotional condition. The doctor thought it best to keep her under mild sedation for the next forty-eight hours.

When the chaplain called on Mrs. C again two days later he found her rested and more coherent although still suffering emotional shock. Her first remark was "Why did God let this happen to me? What have I done to be punished?" The chaplain allowed Mrs. C ample time to pour out her anguish and grief over this tragedy. Then he attempted to explain to her that this could happen to any person and that it was not necessarily a punishment of God upon her as one individual singled out of the human race. "The majority of us carry defective genes," he said, "and no one can tell when one of these abnormal genes will come forth in the time of reproduction, or when environmental factors may produce an abnormality."

Mrs. C was already the mother of two healthy boys and had very much wanted this child to be a girl. As she discussed her doubts there was no movement on her part toward a confession and no indication of any specific or real sin and guilt to complicate her problem of adjustment.

In closing his interview, the chaplain read to her what Jesus said in reply to a question much the same as hers: "Master, who did sin, this man, or his parents, that he was born blind? Jesus answered, Neither hath this man sinned, nor his parents: but that the works of God should be made manifest in him" (John 9:2-3). In the prayer which followed the chaplain voiced Mrs. C's bewilderment at this unexplainable event which had happened to her and asked that God give her the faith and courage to make whatever decisions were necessary for the proper care of this child, by the grace of God.

On his final visit with Mrs. C the chaplain found that she and her husband were beginning to face up to the reality of the situation and were making plans for the care of this child and what they would say to the other children. The chaplain supported her in her sense of obligation to the boys and suggested that on her return home she might read Dale Rogers' *Angel Unawares,* or Pearl Buck's story of *The Child Who Never Grew.*

Obviously the chaplain's ministry to Mrs. C was largely one of support since this was her primary need at the time. She began to accept to some extent the reality of her situation while in the hospital but would still face heartache and grief in making the adjustments that must necessarily arise in the family circle. In addition to the practical problems of caring for a blind and hopelessly crippled child she was also recovering from a psychological blow to her ego. The individual should not feel this way, but to produce a deformed child causes the parents to feel defective. All of this indicates Mrs. C's need for a sustained pastoral relationship.

Ministering to parents of a malformed child is a demanding task which requires understanding and the use of various resources.

1. A form of grief accompanies the birth of an abnormal child. The parents are shocked by the shattering of their hopes and dreams. A certain amount of time is required regardless of any help they may receive to recuperate and adjust to this painful reality. In contrast to the bereavement connected with the stillborn child this is a more indecisive type of grief. The parents want to love and accept the child but are grieved over his deformity.

2. Guilt often arises in the minds of the parents of a malformed child. As the parents search for a reason why, they scrutinize their former lives for any sins committed or mistakes that were made. Most people can usually find something. One such couple confessed that they had engaged in premarital intimacies. Among other incidents with which this guilt may be connected are extramarital relationships, masturbation, venereal disease, or rejection of the pregnancy. The pastor should be alert for any indications of a need for confession. This guilt is important whether real or imaginary.

3. Comfort and support, rather than psychological exploration,

is the first need of the distraught parent. When Mrs. C said, "Why did God let this happen to me? What have I done to be punished?" the chaplain certainly would not say, "So you feel you are being punished?" This is no time to reflect absurdly the person's statements. If the minister is ever going to have anything to say that will give spiritual support now is the time to say it.

4. Medical science can offer valuable help in overcoming or reducing the seriousness of many malformations. When a reputable doctor says that repair is indicated the pastor should support the parents in this decision. On the other hand, when a reputable doctor advises that nothing can be done the pastor should discourage the parents from running from one clinic to another over the country, as so frequently happens, which accomplishes nothing except the depletion of the family finances.

5. There are social resources that offer help to the parents of the malformed child. The pastor may guide the parents to a rehabilitation service, custodial home, mental hygiene clinic, or other needed resource. Parents of a malformed child should be introduced to other parents having had a similar experience. In some communities there are organized parents' groups which meet regularly for fellowship and the promotion of community interest in the problems of the handicapped.

Another difficult pastoral care situation related to childbirth is that of ministering to a mother whose child is born out of wedlock. No one knows precisely how many out-of-wedlock children are born in the United States each year, but the National Office of Vital Statistics gave 201,700 as the estimate for 1957, the last published count available.[5] The need for concealment explains the fact that the unmarried mother is more often seen on the maternity service of large city hospitals and medical centers than in small community hospitals. The mother often must manage her pregnancy apart from family and friends due to the social stigma attached to illegitimate parenthood.

The unmarried mother and her parents if she confides in them often try to keep her pregnancy concealed. Mary came to the city, contacted an obstetrician, and stayed in a hotel until her baby was due. When she entered the hospital there was not a private room available and she was placed in a four-bed ward. The delivery was uncomplicated.

The chaplain saw her on the day following the birth of her baby and found her quite uncommunicative and withdrawn from the other patients in the ward. From the conversation it was obvious that she was depressed and under a good deal of emotional strain. After two or three "yes" and "no" responses, the chaplain said, "I can see that you don't feel like talking today. I'll be back to see you later."

In the meantime her obstetrician called the chaplain to tell him that he had a young patient who needed help. "I told her I was going to call you and ask you to spend some time with her," he said.

The chaplain called again on the following day and as he sat down beside the bed, said, "Mary, your doctor told me about your circumstances and asked me to come by to see you. I know you are a good ways from home; I work here all the time and if I can help you in any way I want you to feel free to use me."

Mary was an attractive nineteen-year-old girl whose parents were both living. She had a sister two years younger. She confided in her mother and the two of them concealed the whole experience from her father. Her father and mother had always disagreed and the three women in the family always banded together. When the mother learned of the pregnancy, she confessed to Mary that her own marriage took place because she was pregnant. The mother, who ran the family budget, secured the money and made all the plans to get Mary away from home to have the baby. Her explicit advice to Mary was that she not see the child, but let it be placed for adoption.

Mary said that the father of her child was a close friend she knew through high school but she did not love him and had no desire to marry him. She said she had been to Sunday School all her life and did not know how she could ever have gotten herself into such an awful predicament.

The chaplain said in response that all of us make mistakes in life, but some of these mistakes create more problems than others. "You are young and your life is still ahead of you," he said. "I am

interested in you as a person and what you are going to let this
experience do to you."

"When I first began to worry, I cried myself to sleep many
nights and prayed to God that it would not be so," Mary said. "To
be honest with you, chaplain, I have not tried to pray since."

"You have condemned yourself a great deal in the last nine
months, haven't you?" asked the chaplain. "You know, the real
problem for most of us lies in our inability to forgive ourselves. God
is willing and anxious to forgive us anytime we come to Him with
genuine and sincere repentance. But, Mary, Jesus said this much
better than I can say it." He handed her his New Testament opened
to the eighth chapter of the Gospel of John and asked her to read
the first eleven verses. After a pause, the chaplain asked, "Do you
see what Jesus said to a girl in a similar situation: '. . . Neither do
I condemn thee: go, and sin no more'?" She replied, "I do want His
forgiveness." The chaplain prayed that she would be able to accept
God's forgiveness and that He would guide her in the decision she
must make about her baby.

Before leaving, the chaplain secured Mary's permission to call
a caseworker from the local Family and Child Care Agency to come
and talk over her future plans. Mary decided before leaving the
hospital that she would let an adoption agency find her baby a good
home and as she put it "have a chance in life." She also agreed to
let the chaplain get in touch with her local pastor and promised to go
to him for more intensive counseling after she reached home.

There are certainly individual differences in the personality
background of unmarried mothers, but it is almost unbelievable how
many of them present the same general characteristics. Our impression of the unmarried mother, derived from the records of our out-
patient pastoral counseling service over a period of years, closely
coincides with the findings presented by Leontine Young in her
book, *Out of Wedlock*.

The unmarried mother, contrary to popular opinion, is not a
sexually promiscuous girl. More often than not she becomes pregnant
by a man she has little or no interest in as a prospective husband.
He serves primarily as a biological tool for the fulfillment of her

unconscious need. For this reason the pastor-counselor should not "jump in" immediately to try to "get these people married." A marriage license guarantees neither a happy marital adjustment nor a healthy environment for a child that did not ask to be born.

Usually the girl comes from a home where she has been almost completely dominated by one parent, either the father or the mother. This was true in Mary's case. Her own mother was forced into marriage because she was pregnant with Mary and her oversolicitous dominating nature tells us that she had not loved her daughter in a healthy manner. Mary may have sensed this, but did not realize the real cause behind her own blind actions. Her unconscious need to have a baby is her way of getting back at her mother and also her father with whom she had a very unsatisfactory relationship. Understanding these dynamics will help the pastor to realize how much the unmarried mother is in need of sympathetic guidance in finding herself. There is no need for condemning these girls; society takes care of that!

Obviously a girl so unconsciously motivated as to get pregnant to spite her parents is not emotionally prepared in most instances for motherhood. She tends to see the child as a "baby" rather than an individual who will one day grow into maturity. Hence the pastor, doctor, and caseworker are often the only spokesmen for the rights of the helpless child.

A girl may be dead set on keeping her child without any awareness of the difficulty involved in working, placing the child in a day nursery, and caring for it at night. When a girl is blindly "loving" her baby without being able to make clear-cut decisions about financial arrangements or working conditions, it may be better that she offer the child for adoption through a recognized agency that will protect the child's welfare. On the other hand, there are many instances in which a relative may be willing to provide foster care. Later, if the girl makes a successful marriage, she may be able to recover her child. All of this means that the pastor should not push the mother toward a particular decision but should provide her with as many facts as possible as she determines her own baby's future.

The unmarried mother's sense of shame is in some instances reinforced by one of the parents. A typical statement to the chaplain in the presence of the girl is, "I don't know how in the world she could do this to us. She has never given us any trouble before, and after all we have tried to do for her!" To cut the girl loose from this pious bondage it may become necessary for the pastor to be very directive. In talking to one father privately, a chaplain said, "Let me ask you a question, 'Have you at any time in your life made a mistake along this line?'" The father fumblingly admitted that before he married he had done some things of which he was ashamed. The chaplain said, "The only reason you didn't get pregnant then was that you didn't have a womb! Really, in the spirit of Christ, don't you think all of us ought to do all we can to keep this experience from ruining your daughter's life? You know, in the final analysis there is only one class of people. We are all sinners in one way or another. Your daughter needs you as a father with your love and understanding like she has never needed you before." Directive handling of a manipulating parent may help him to get his mind off his daughter's weakness long enough to see his own and thereby stimulate a spirit of forgiveness.

The unmarried mother often needs to be referred to a home for maternity care and may need a foster home to care for her baby while she makes a decision. The pastor will find social casework a valuable adjunct to his ministry and should know the family and child care resources in his state and community.

Unmarried parents need all the guidance they can get. The hospital chaplain rarely sees the father, and the limits of time affect his work with the mother. If the pastor has access to both parents he can examine the relationship of the boy and girl to see whether or not marriage is a possibility. In any case he will want to make intensive counseling available.

Regardless of whether a new baby is normal, malformed, or born out of wedlock, he deserves the best the human race has to offer. It is the task of the church to see that the child receives his rightful heritage.

For Use in Pastoral Care

Buck, Pearl. *The Child Who Never Grew.* New York: John Day Company, 1950.

Brenneman, Helen Good. *Meditations for the New Mother.* Scottsdale, Pa.: Herald Press, 1953.

Calling All Parents. Chicago (535 N. Dearborn): American Medical Association.

Hymes, James L. *Enjoy Your Child—Ages 1, 2 and 3.* (FL. 141). New York (22 East 38th St.): Public Affairs Pamphlets.

Infant Care. Children's Bureau Publication No. 8. For sale by the Superintendent of Documents, U.S. Government Printing Office, Washington 25, D.C.

Reid, Francis P. *None So Small.* Nashville: Broadman Press, 1958.

Winnicott, D. W. *Mother and Child, A Primer of First Relationships.* New York: Basic Books, 1957.

For Further Reading

Capa, Cornell, and Pines, Maya. *Retarded Children Can Be Helped.* Great Neck, N. Y.: Channel Press, 1957.

Deutsch, Helene. *The Psychology of Women.* New York: Grune and Stratton, 1944-1945. II:202-93, 332-92.

Hillard, Marian. *A Woman Doctor Looks at Love and Life.* Garden City, N. Y.: Doubleday and Company, 1957. Pp. 17-31.

Kemp, Charles F. *The Church: The Gifted and the Retarded Child.* St. Louis: The Bethany Press, 1957.

Rank, Otto. *The Trauma of Birth.* New York: Harcourt Brace and Company, 1929.

Waller, Willard. *The Family, A Dynamic Interpretation.* Revised by Reuben Hill. New York: The Dryden Press, 1951. Pp. 375-93.

White, Park J. "Helping Parents of Congenitally Malformed Children," *Religion and Health,* 1:23-28, Sept. 1952.

Young, Leontine. *Out of Wedlock, A Study of the Problems of the Unmarried Mother and Her Child.* New York: McGraw-Hill Book Company, 1954.

TEN *Spiritual Therapy during the Involutional Period*

The choir, along with the minister, had assembled and was about to move into the sanctuary for the morning worship service when Mrs. P, a slightly gray forty-eight-year-old housewife, spoke up excitedly:

"Pastor, we just must do something for the visiting minister this evening. If the choir would like to entertain, I'll make some punch and get some cookies from the store for a social hour afterwards."

The pastor said privately to the visiting minister: "What she will do is go home, bake about four hundred cookies, make the punch, and if there is any time left she will start telephoning to be sure everyone is present tonight. Then after the program is over, she will not be able to sleep a wink and neither will her husband."

A short time later Mrs. P, who was in the middle of "the change of life," was referred to a medical center for a checkup by her family physician. Every hospital chaplain is aware of how many patients in this age group enter the hospital for physical examinations which turn out negative.

The chaplain's first contact with Mrs. J came at ten o'clock one night when he was called to the hospital and found her walking

The authors wish to acknowledge their gratitude to Wingate M. Johnson, M.D., Professor (Emeritus) of Clinical Internal Medicine, Bowman Gray School of Medicine and North Carolina Baptist Hospital, for contributing to this chapter and reading the whole for medical accuracy.

the corridor, wringing her hands, despite the fact that she had received a maximum dose of sedative. She had experienced anxiety, insomnia, exhaustion, and bouts of mild despondency for several months prior to admission. The chaplain and the nurse accompanied her back to her bed where the chaplain let her talk for about thirty minutes. On this occasion and in subsequent visits, she told the following story:

At the age of twenty she married an energetic young man who had just become affiliated with a large company. He worked hard and in the course of time earned successive promotions, but had little time for social life or for his family. During these strenuous years their three children were born. Thus Mrs. P necessarily received more and more of her emotional satisfaction from her children, while her husband's came from his business associates. They began their marriage with love and high ideals, but grew apart so gradually that neither ever realized what was happening until one day they met face to face in a beautiful home empty of children.

About this time Mrs. P entered the menopause and a year later came into the hospital because of her growing agitation. All the physical findings during her examination were essentially negative. The doctors explained to her the very real biological changes which were taking place and encouraged her to try to forget herself and to find some new interests. In talking with the chaplain about this she said, "I have everything in the world I need to be happy. I'm proud of my children; we have a beautiful home and no financial worries, and yet I am more unhappy than I have ever been in my life. In fact, chaplain, I'm ashamed of myself. I'm supposed to be a good Christian woman."

The chaplain explained that the Christian, like anyone else, is subject to the many pressures of life. "I think the doctor has something, though, when he mentioned your need to find some new interests in life," he said. "Have you given any thought to this?" After talking for some time she decided that since she did not hold an office in her church she would volunteer for service in the mission Sunday School.

Mrs. P was discharged from the hospital on the third day. It was obvious that her problem was aggravated by a strong situational factor. Her emotional needs were not being met by her husband and the bodily changes of involution served to focus her thoughts inward. Her medical examination relieved her mind, and her doctor gave her a thorough explanation of how best to weather this trying period. Although his ministry was rather superficial, the chaplain did attempt to direct Mrs. P toward a consideration of areas of interest that would help her add more depth to her life.

Some understanding of the biological and psychological factors related to the climacteric will help to place in better perspective the pastoral care of persons in this stage of life. The term "climacteric" is derived from a Greek word which means "rung of the ladder" and serves to denote a critical epoch of life.[1] Menopause simply means cessation of the menses, whereas climacteric is a word used to cover the experience of both men and women.

Life is a succession of critical events which call for readjustment and growth. Birth, puberty, adolescence, marriage, and parenthood are all crises which occur to both male and female, and the climacteric with its associated changes is another event which must be met.

Irregular and unpredictable menstruation is the most obvious signal that a woman is entering the involutional period. It occurs roughly between forty and fifty years of age. From a biological standpoint menopause is accompanied by changes in hormonal activity. Vasomotor disturbances produce hot flashes, sensations of dizziness, and profuse sweats which are sometimes accompanied by headaches and neuralgias. These physical complaints stemming from glandular changes may be accompanied by psychological symptoms such as insomnia, anxiety states, excitability, and depression. The cessation of ovarian activity tends to disturb the balance of the remainder of the endocrine system.[2]

Endocrine changes are a fact, but the emotional reaction to these changes may be affected by one's psychological conditioning. Traditions and superstitions concerning "the change" can be as destructive as old wives' tales about childbirth. As one woman doctor puts it, "Generations of panicky women have spawned enough

untruths about the menopause to panic the next five generations." [3]
The personality structure of the individual will determine whether
or not she will use these bodily changes as an excuse, for example, to turn loose irritability that has been held back.

From a psychologic standpoint Helene Deutsch observes a natural tendency for unsolved problems of earlier stages to arise. [4]
Unsolved problems are carried over to every stage of life, but
especially so at this period. The preclimacterium is comparable to
prepuberty. Just as is the case then, there is a thrust of activity,
and all the forces of the self are mobilized to achieve a better adjustment to reality. Old values tend to crumble away and a desire
to experience something new and exciting makes itself felt. Who
has not heard of the many warnings concerning a "last fling" in
middle life? By middle age most people have adolescent children
who are cutting themselves loose from home. This fact serves to
remind them of their own struggle for independence and may awaken
unresolved conflicts.

The biological changes may result in two entirely opposite
types of reaction. One is a tendency to become introspective. For
example, a person who has failed to attain certain goals in life
can become morbidly preoccupied. In extreme cases this introspection may manifest itself in severe depression. Women whose desire
for children is unfulfilled may react strongly to this change. Deutsch
depicts the influence of this biological fact when she says: "At
the moment when expulsion of ova from the ovary ceases, all the
organic processes devoted to the service of the species stop. Woman
has ended her existence as bearer of a future life, and has reached
her natural end—her partial death—as servant of the species. She
is now engaged in an active struggle against her decline." [5]

The opposite reaction to introspection is the tendency toward
overactivity. The whole experience means a sharp break with the
past. The heightened psychic vitality causes the individual to want
to begin life all over again. Some women have been known to
start a diary, dig up old love letters, or engage in fantasy about
a first husband or sweetheart. There may be changes in their attitude toward the family or husband. If they are unable to control

their activity and act out their fantasies they appear to relive their adolescence all over again. Acting-out usually indicates a hysterical disposition. Some individuals escape into an ascetic form of life and become overzealous in the expression of their religious belief. They tend to be highly suggestible. Many ministers at some time or another have had the experience of dealing with the individual who responds each time he gives an invitation to religious commitment.

Similarities in personality make-up have been found among women experiencing severe difficulty with this period of life. These people have previously tended to be sensitive and to live a rather isolated social life. They may boast about staying at home minding their own business, thus making a virtue out of their fear of associating with people. Usually strict and pedantic in the training of their children, they are likely to be meticulous about cleanliness, sexually frigid, ungenerous and prone to be critical, and emotionally and spiritually impoverished.[6]

In some cases there is a tendency to become highly suspicious. Two spinsters who were living together during the menopause became distrustful of each other. When one setting the table would forget a piece of silver or the salt shaker, the other would accuse her of doing this on purpose. The result was constant bickering between them.

Many of the same emotional reactions that can accompany menopause in women may also appear in men. Of course, men have no biological counterpart to the menopause. Instead of an obvious event, there is simply a gradual slowing down of hormonal activity through the years. In general, medical science prefers to restrict the use of the term "male climacteric" to specific illnesses that might impair the sexual adequacy of the male at this time and to designate the general phase in both men and women as the "involutional period." [7]

Ordinarily men reach their greatest productivity during the middle years. At the same time their parental, vocational, and social responsibilities have multiplied. If the man has achieved marital, business, and social success he is less likely to experience impotence or revert to sexual promiscuity, alcoholism, or drug addiction during the involutional period.

The emotional reactions of men during this period, like that of women, are explained on the basis of earlier conflicts in the personality. The vocational area is one of the most vulnerable spots in the psychic economy of the male.

In the same way that the woman's life tends to be organized around the vocation of motherhood the life of the man tends to be centered around productivity in his vocation. Hence any event which threatens to block his achievement of vocational satisfaction may disturb a man emotionally just as deeply as the inability to bear children may disturb a woman.

If a man has been overconcerned about his sexual potency all along, he is more likely to be tempted to prove himself with a "last fling" in middle life than the more secure individual. Both husbands and wives experiencing difficulty during the climacteric often meet with misunderstanding from each other. In some instances the minister may help a husband or wife to become more tolerant of the spouse during this trying period.

More than one person passing through the involutional period has been hurt by his friends' lack of understanding of his behavior. The pastor will not only encounter persons in the involutional period as he visits the sick in his hospital, but will confront the more mild emotional reactions of these persons in his daily contacts. Frequently he will observe the person's stress before the person himself has recognized his need of medical attention. This is especially true of mild depression.

There are several ways in which these people will come to the attention of the pastor. Some will express their tendency toward overactivity by becoming involved in church work to the point of neglecting their homes. Before Mrs. P entered the hospital she would volunteer for any job that came along. The resultant stress kept her, and often her husband, awake.[8] There is nothing wrong with giving these people something to do, but they should not be exploited. The pastor can easily have a blind spot here, especially when he lacks lay leadership in the church.

Occasionally a woman will apologize to the pastor for her inability to be in a crowd or sit through the church service. Her anxiety is very real. If she could sit comfortably in a theater, there might be some question, but this person gets anxious in a crowd anywhere. Recognizing that the person is already feeling guilty, the pastor will show understanding by saying, "I know these feelings are very real to you." He could suggest that she sit at the rear or near a door and leave whenever she feels the need to do so.

An experienced Sunday School teacher may suddenly suffer fright in public speaking. One woman recalled that her first sensation of a "hot flash" came while she was standing in front of her class of adult women. She managed to get through the lesson, but was "scared stiff." This fear continued to build up in her mind, until she sought counseling help. Urging such a person to continue her teaching may force her into the embarrassing position of explaining the reasons for her intense feelings.

Dedicated men may sometimes become lax in their morals. Practically every church has experienced the loss of one valuable man through a character breakdown during involution. A forty-eight-year-old man who for years had been active in his church was suspected of having an affair with his secretary. Instead of listening to gossip and neglecting an individual who needed help, this man's pastor went to him and offered his services. "Look, John," he said, "I am running the risk of losing your friendship by sticking my nose into your business without having been asked. There may be no factual basis whatever for what I have heard, but there is gossip going around about you and your secretary. If you say the word I will leave this minute, but as your pastor I think too much of you to stand by without offering help if you need it."

John accepted the pastor's offer of help and in the course of several hours of counseling finally decided that he must make a choice. Realizing that this was a passing phase, he decided to remain with his wife.

Neither the doctor nor the lawyer ordinarily offer their services until they are asked. Even though it is impossible to help an individual until he wants help, the pastor's traditional role demands that he offer his services to members of his church when they are in trouble. In such circumstances the pastor often fails, but he will fail less often if he takes a nonjudgmental attitude.

A woman in the involutional period may come to the pastor's attention because of her suspicions of her husband which have no basis in fact. One minister serving a field of two churches had been asked to resign by one of them as a result of a whispering campaign his wife had been carrying on behind his back. The church was reluctant to give the real reason for its action, but when the minister finally learned the truth he arranged for his wife to go to a medical center for a checkup. The doctors found mild paranoid tendencies complicating her adjustment to the change of life. After the chaplain had talked with the doctor and received the results of the examination he wrote a letter to the chairman of the board of deacons and the minister was reinstated.

Finally, the pastor will encounter persons in the involutional period who are concerned with having committed the "unpardonable sin" or with having lost their relationship to God. These feelings are almost always connected with mild or severe depression. The pastor will not attempt counseling with these persons except in close co-operation with a physician. However, the pastor can help such persons to realize that their religious concerns are symptoms of their emotional condition. For example, ask the individual, "Is the sun as bright, do things seem as real and alive to you as they have been?" The depressed person will answer, "No." Then the pastor can say, "We use the same emotions to worship God as we do to appreciate a sunset." This will not get the individual well, but can keep him from being upset over being upset.

To accept the fact that one is sick is the first step toward getting well. In the early stages of depression the individual does not realize that he is sick and continues to expect the same performance from himself that he did prior to his illness. In explaining this the pastor may say, "A depression is no respecter of persons, and therefore is no reflection upon your Christian life. If you had a broken leg, you would not expect to get up and walk. There are doctors trained to deal with this emotional condition just as there are doctors trained to set a broken leg." The pastor can render a signal service if he can convince these people of the need for specialized help in the early stages of their depression.

An examination of the psychological factors which characterize middle life leads to several practical conclusions:

1. Guide these people to proper help in cases of depression. Any depressed person is potentially capable of suicide. Suicidal thoughts may not always be expressed, but if the person has a tendency to wake up in the early hours of the morning it is a danger signal. Of course the direct question, "Have you thought of taking your life?" is not in order, but the pastor may say, "Have you ever thought of just giving in to all these pressures?" This sort of question often leads the individual to say, "Yes, I've even thought of taking my life, but as a Christian I can't let myself think like that." When the pastor suspects strong suicidal tendencies he should advise some responsible member of the family to seek medical attention for the depressed person.

When talking with the family there is no place for dogmatic assertions. Simply say, "I don't want to alarm you, and I may be completely wrong, but I am somewhat concerned about his will to live. If he were a member of my family, I would call in a physician."

2. Capitalize on the person's desire for new experience, especially the creative urge among women. For example, some of these individuals could be given completely new jobs in the church that call for initative, originality, and creative ability. One such person was told, "Here is an age level we are having difficulty reaching. Maybe you can figure out a project or some way to interest these young people."

3. Reach these people for Christ. The middle years, like adolescence, produce changes which are conducive to finding a new way of life. If a person passes through this period without experiencing repentance and a change in the direction of his loyalties, the tragic truth is the chances are slim that he will ever change.

Until middle life the individual was justified in his inner feeling that life was expanding, but now he must face the fact that physically he has reached the top rung of the ladder and the remainder of his journey will be gradually downward. Doors which were open during young maturity have been closed by middle age and other avenues of expression must be found.

Our culture, with its emphasis on youth, makes it difficult for the average person to shift his emotional gears to correspond with his increasing physical limitations. There is a temptation to postpone preparation for old age, and middle life affords the last real opportunity to expand one's interests. How many times do you hear statements such as this: "When I retire, I'm going to do so and so." It is too late to build up resources for old age after it arrives. If one has not already built a base of broad interests in life old age is likely to be barren.

The important thing in facing the latter stages of life is that we have the necessary spiritual resources for dealing with any problems that arise. As spiritual guide, the pastor can encourage his people to cultivate the gardens of the spirit in such a way that they achieve spiritual maturity simultaneously with physical maturity.

For Further Reading

BILLIG, OTTO, AND ADAMS, ROBERT. "Emotional Problems of the Middle Aged Man," *Psychiatric Quarterly*, 28:442-52, July 1954.

DEUTSCH, HELENE. *The Psychology of Women*—2 vols. New York: Grune and Stratton, 1944-45. II:456-87.

GRAY, MADELINE. *The Changing Years*. Garden City, N. Y.: Doubleday and Company, 1951.

HILLIARD, MARIAN. *A Woman Doctor Looks at Love and Life*. Garden City, N. Y.: Doubleday and Company, 1957.

HOWE, REUEL. *The Creative Years*. Greenwich, Conn.: Seabury Press, 1959.

JOHNSON, WINGATE M. *The Years After Fifty*. New York: Whittlesey House, 1947.

WEISS, EDWARD, AND ENGLISH, O. SPURGEON. *Psychosomatic Medicine*. Philadelphia: W. B. Saunders Company, 1957. Pp. 375-82, 404-8.

ELEVEN *Spiritual Therapy for the Acutely Bereaved*

A twelve-year-old girl had been fishing in the farm lake. She started back to the house thinking her two-and-a-half-year-old brother was following her, but upon turning around she saw him leaning over, trying to pick a waterlily. Yelling a warning, she ran back, caught hold of him, and said, "If you had fallen into that water, we would have to dig a deep dark hole in the ground and throw dirt in on top of you." The scene she painted was so vivid it made the little brother cry, and she then proceeded to comfort him. The next morning the child followed his mother across the highway to the mailbox, was struck by a passing car, and instantly killed. Three days after she had pictured the burial scene to her brother, the girl was standing in the cemetery watching men lower his body into the ground.

This young girl was unable to cry or express her feelings during the funeral and did not share what had happened between her and her brother with her parents or minister. Seven years later while in nursing school, she requested an appointment with the chaplain and described her condition in the following way.

"I do not know what is wrong with me. I cry easily. I know my

The authors wish to acknowledge their gratitude to Richard C. Proctor, M.D., Assistant Professor of Psychiatry, Bowman Gray School of Medicine and North Carolina Baptist Hospital, for reading this chapter for medical accuracy.

grades are going down because I cannot concentrate. I have just never been this way before."

She became somewhat attached to an elderly lady, whom she had nursed for the two weeks prior to the patient's death. The expiration of her patient awakened unresolved grief in the student nurse which resulted in a mild depression. When in the course of several hours of counseling she was able to relive her grief over the death of her brother and cry out her feelings which were blocked up earlier, her depression cleared away.

This case serves to illustrate what Helene Deutsch[1] and Erich Lindemann[2] have referred to as postponed or delayed grief reaction and signifies further the strategic role of the pastor in aiding bereaved persons to begin their grief work in a healthy manner. Beginning with Freud's original study, "Mourning and Melancholia,"[3] the psychological process of bereavement has been studied intensively, and the psychiatric literature describing the grief process has been adapted to the pastoral ministry in a competent manner by such men as Rogers,[4] Irion,[5] and Jackson.[6] Little clinical research, however, has been done by clergymen themselves regarding the use of their role and religious resources as related to the grief process. This chapter is an attempt in this direction since it is based upon a study of the immediate reactions to death by the family in a hospital setting.

During a two-year period, the Department of Pastoral Care at the North Carolina Baptist Hospital kept clinical notes on the chaplain's ministry to three hundred thirty-one families at the time of expiration. The setting for his contact with the family was a parlor adjacent to the chapel where all bereaved families were taken to meet with the doctor and the chaplain. Certain questions served as a guide to the recording of these clinical notes:

1. What was the family's first statement upon learning of the death?
2. What was the age and family role of the deceased?
3. How many members of the family were present?
4. What were the general characteristics of the family's grief reaction?
5. How long did the chaplain spend with the family?

6. How did the family relate to the minister? What religious resources were used?
7. How did the family relate to the doctor? State whether or not permission was obtained for an autopsy.
8. Record any other pertinent or significant information.

An inductive method of analysis was used to examine these bereavement write-ups.[7] The resultant picture should be helpful to the pastor in understanding the meaning of what is usually encountered in the acute stages of bereavement.

Upon learning of the death of a loved one the family almost invariably exhibits bewilderment, crying, a need to talk of the deceased, and in some cases extreme reactions of hostility, guilt, and shock. Bewilderment, a state of confusion, or a sensation of "lostness" was experienced by 95 per cent of the families studied. For the first few minutes simple routines could not be performed. It was rather typical, for example, for a next of kin to be unable to give the telephone number of his home. "What am I going to do?" was a common expression of this bewilderment.

Intense bewilderment was noted in thirty-eight families, thirty-five of which involved women and five of which involved men (two families showed this reaction in both sexes simultaneously). The degree of bewilderment seems to be related to the intensity of the relationship which is broken by death. Of the thirty-eight families who experienced intense bewilderment, twenty-three were wives who had lost husbands, seven were children who lost parents, seven were parents who lost a child, one was a husband who lost a wife.

The value of preparing the family for bereavement when possible is suggested by the fact that in twenty-six of the thirty-eight cases of extreme bewilderment death was unexpected and was therefore more of a shock to the family. Another fact pointing in this direction was the absence of bewilderment noted in thirteen cases. In every one of these cases the deceased was an elderly adult, which suggested that death was anticipated and therefore more readily accepted by the bereaved.

The second most frequent manifestation of initial grief was a need to talk about the deceased, to review the circumstances preceding the death and to idealize him, as noted in 94 per cent of the 331 families studied. A daughter who had lost her sixty-five-year-old mother said, "She suffered so much. I could hear her all the way to the elevator last night. She was a wonderful mother."

In fifteen cases the need to talk about the deceased was unusually intense, as noted when the bereaved person talked but seemed oblivious to his surroundings. As in the symptom of bewilderment, the majority of these cases (twelve of fifteen) involved women, seven were wives who had lost husbands, and seven felt that the death was unexpected.

A third common element in the grief reaction was weeping. Talking or thinking about the deceased seemed to stimulate the crying which was observed in 83 per cent of the total cases. The amount or intensity of weeping varied widely. Some individuals by nature appeared more stoical while others reacted more readily to emotional stimulus. In a majority of cases there was profuse to moderate weeping, while thirty-one revealed hysterical or uncontrollable crying, and fifty-six wept hardly at all.

Hysterical weeping was manifested mainly by women. A woman whose husband was brought to the hospital and died unexpectedly from a brain hemorrhage cried uncontrollably for forty-five minutes. She continued to cry out, "He's gone, O my Lord! O Jesus!" and not even the best efforts of a large family could calm her. Seventeen of the thirty-one individuals whose weeping was intense were wives stricken with grief over the loss of husbands.

Another case of hysterical crying involved a wife whose father's funeral was scheduled the same day her husband died. Her husband was in the hospital and supposedly doing well when he suddenly died. The family was contacted just as they were leaving to go to the father's funeral. The wife was the mother of six children under twelve years of age and during the uncontrollable sobbing that came from this double bereavement she cried out, "How will I tell the children?"

Hysterical weeping was prevalent in the reactions of three men out of the total of thirty-one instances. There were fifty-six families who showed no crying at all. Forty-two of these fifty-six families where there was no crying consisted of men.

The number of family members present at the time of death ranged from one to twenty-three, but the most frequent number present was two (one hundred six cases). There were three people present in sixty-nine cases and four present in forty-one cases. There were five or more members of the family present in sixty-nine cases. The most frequent family role among the relatives present was that of the children of the deceased, since children were present in one hundred twenty-one cases. Wives were the next more frequently bereaved relative, numbering one hundred eight, whereas husbands were present in only fifty-two cases. A parent of the deceased was present in seventy-seven cases. In many situations one or two family members were present at the time of death and waited for the arrival of other relatives, before a decision was made concerning autopsy and the selection of a funeral home. In general, the notes on the cases suggested that the presence of a larger group of relatives tended to facilitate a healthy beginning of grief work since the family members supported one another.

The predominant age of the deceased was above sixty years. This group composed 35.2 per cent of the total expirations. Next in frequency were deaths of people in the middle years (thirty-sixty) which amounted to 31.1 per cent of the deceased. Infants under two years came next in frequency, comprising 14.5 per cent of the deaths, and the loss of children, teen-agers and young adults combined was less than 20 per cent.

An evaluation of the manner in which death was accepted by the family was made by noting the presence or absence of such factors as guilt, blaming oneself for the death, resentment directed toward other family members, the doctor, or toward God, and whether there seemed to be a sincere expression of emotion and a healthy acceptance of the reality of death. On the basis of these criteria, one hundred sixty-three families out of three hundred thirty-one seemed to accept the reality of death realistically and demonstrated a healthy outpouring of their feelings. At least seventy-nine of the bereaved families maintained sufficient poise in the midst of the crisis to make some tangible expression of appreciation toward the hospital, the doctors, the nurses, and the chaplain.

Some of the less frequent but none the less significant grief responses recorded were shock, guilt, and hostility. An appreciable degree of shock was manifested by sixty-four families as illustrated by such statements as: "He's not dead—he's not dead!"—"I can't believe it!"—"We didn't know she was that sick!"

Clear-cut evidence of guilt feelings was present in twenty-eight of the three hundred thirty-one families. It was expressed in such statements as: "Chaplain, I killed him just as sure as if I had shot him. He would not have had this heart attack if he had not traveled a long distance to get me out of trouble."—"The Lord took my child because I have not carried out my promises to Him about my church."—"O God, I was not as close to him as I should have been."—"Oh, why didn't I stop drinking when she pleaded with me so much."

Expressions of resentment and hostility were made by twenty-nine of the three hundred thirty-one familes studied. A wife whose husband was killed in an accident while helping a friend cried out, "Why did it happen to him? That's what you get for doing people a favor. God didn't give him a chance!" A father shouted as he pounded the wall of the conference room, "He's mine. You can't take him!" The minister had to support him physically at times before he could recover control of himself.

In teaching hospitals, an autopsy or post-mortem examination must be performed on a certain percentage of all expirations to maintain the accreditation of the institution. The reason for this is that the autopsy provides the best-known method of studying the effect of the treatment procedure used against the illness and is an index to the hospital's standard of medical practice. Usually the doctor informs the family, first of all, of the death, gives a brief description of how death occurred, and expresses his regret at being unable to save the deceased before making a request for autopsy. At this time the chaplain supplements the doctor's ministry to the family and can often influence the family to grant permission for a post-mortem examination.

Permission for an autopsy was granted in two out of every three cases in this study, but considerable resistance was encountered in other cases. The brother of a man who possibly committed suicide exclaimed, "When a man's going to die, a doctor can't stop it! It's God's business why he died, and not the doctor's." This family, in all probability, did not want to know the truth. The husband, in another situation, said of his thirty-year-old wife who died following heart surgery, "Several days ago she said she hoped there wouldn't be any more cutting on her. She wanted to be left in peace." A mother of an eighteen-year-old boy when asked about giving his eyes and arteries for transplant said, "I can't stand to think of part of my boy walking around in someone else, though I know it would help someone."

The bereavement write-ups showed that the chaplain was almost universally well-received by the bereaved family. The high incidence of acceptance of the minister probably reflects both the regional culture and the setting of this study in a denominationally owned hospital. There was evidence of definite hostility toward the minister by a member of the family in eight out of three hundred thirty-one situations. When a lady requested the chaplain to pray with the family her sister said, "No siree, I don't want to pray to a God who would let my mother suffer like she did."

Prayer was the religious resource most often used by the chaplain apart from the symbolic significance of his presence with the family in the role of a minister. The use of prayer and scripture with the family prior to their departure from the hospital was recorded in two hundred ninety of the three hundred thirty-one write-ups. The average time spent with a bereaved family by the chaplain was from thirty minutes to an hour.

The analysis of the reactions of the grief-stricken as seen in the hospital can provide clues for making this traditional ministry more effective.

1. The minister's role has special meaning for the family immediately following the death. Comments such as "It's good to have somebody who is close to God with you at a time like this" and "Thank you for coming, chaplain, would you stay with me for a

while?" showed up many times in the bereavement write-ups, signifying the support which the family derived from his presence. Of course it is not always possible for the pastor to be present with the family when death occurs. However, when it is possible, it will strengthen his ministry to the family in the later phases of bereavement.

Because of the bewilderment which almost universally accompanies the news of death, the family needs someone almost to "think for them" in such simple matters as getting them out of the line of traffic on a hospital floor and into a quiet place which every hospital ought to provide for this purpose. In this quiet place, then, the minister can give support and comfort free from unnecessary distractions.

2. Crying is the most common emotional outlet for the person in acute grief. Oftentimes in this study the chaplain observed one member of the family attempting to suppress crying by other members of the family. Common remarks made for this purpose were, "Now look, you've held up well so far, let's not break down now," or "Come on, now, let's not have any more crying. You know mother would not want this." The men in this study cried less frequently than did the women. This could reflect early childhood training when the little boy is told, "Men don't cry. Be a man, now," after he has hurt himself.

When the minister sees that some of the family misunderstand the therapeutic value of crying he can gently move into the situation with some such statement as "The pain of separation is very real. Our sorrow is natural and God understands." Encouraging the expression of grief when it is obvious that the individual is choked up and needs relief can be accomplished in most instances through a simple suggestion: "Go ahead and cry. I would do the same if I were in your place." For the minister to say this helps the person to realize that the maintenance of a stoical attitude is not necessarily a sign of strong Christian faith. Nowhere in the New Testament is the Christian promised exemption from tribulation and pain in this world. He sorrows, but not "as others which have no hope," to use the words of Paul (I Thess. 4:13, AV).

The recent seminary graduate may tend to look upon the more

violent emotional reactions of less educated people as being unhealthy, but he should remember that he arrived at his philosophy of
life after seven years of higher education. Any group behavior that
arises naturally out of the culture must be meeting an emotional need
or else the behavior would never have been adopted. A psychiatrist
has ventured the opinion that there is not as high an incidence of
psychosomatic illnesses resulting from unresolved grief among Negro
patients in the South as among white patients due to the fact that
Negroes often retain the "wake" accompanied by the uninhibited expression of grief surrounding the observance of the funeral.[8] Tears
"wash away" a lot of things if given the opportunity to flow.

To pull away these ceremonial rituals and to insist upon a
highly formal, depersonalized type of funeral may actually do more
harm than good. Any attempts to lift the level of people's responses
must be a gradual process of education and begin where they are
when traditional and cultural factors are involved.

3. Talking about the deceased and the pain of separation helps
the bereaved to face the reality of death. Well-meaning people many
times steer the conversation away from the deceased, when this is the
very topic the bereaved may want and certainly need to talk about.
Showering the individual with cheap, superficial consolation will also
hinder adequate expression.

One theological student suffered the loss of his father while
writing his thesis on "Pastoral Care of the Acutely Bereaved." Upon
his return to the campus he finally became aware that the conversation of all his friends followed the same pattern. They began by saying, "I heard you lost your father," but before the student could say
more than "yes," the friends said "I'm sorry," and started talking immediately about some bereavement they had experienced. After the
student realized that no one really wanted to listen, he made no
further attempt to talk, but resigned himself to listening to others'
tales of woe.

Ninety-four per cent of the families in this study talked freely
about the circumstances surrounding the illness during the chaplain's
brief ministry to them in the hospital. This fact points up the need
for the minister to be a good listener and let the bereaved talk out

his shock and bewilderment. Psychiatric studies have confirmed the value of allowing the bereaved person to verbalize his painful feelings rather than bury them in his unconscious.[9] The pastor may even make an occasion to tell a responsible member of the family the value of encouraging his mother or father, for example, to talk about the loved one during the next several days.

4. The minister should be alert to the more severe grief reactions evidenced by guilt, hostility, and emotional shock. Some degree of shock was noted in sixty-four of the three hundred thirty-one families in the study. A doctor or nurse will minister to the individual in shock in the immediate situation at the hospital. Hostility and guilt showed up in an average of one out of every ten families in the study. Resentment was usually directed toward another member of the family or toward God. Occasionally there were individuals who, feeling guilty over their own neglect, became very hostile toward the hospital, doctor, nurse, or chaplain.

It is inadvisable for the minister to become defensive with these people, because in their state of mind nothing can be accomplished until they have vented their feelings. When God is blamed for taking a life there is no point in the minister becoming unduly anxious. Such individuals in time usually work through these feelings which tend to be exaggerated in the acute phase of grief. With reference to guilt, the pastor should keep in mind that it can be either real or imaginary, but in either case the damaging effect can be serious. Guilt and hostility are both red flags which indicate the need for close pastoral care in the succeeding days.

5. The minister's role, prayer, and scripture are his chief resources for ministering to the bereaved. In the study, scripture and prayer seemed to be appropriate with two hundred ninety families. The guiding principle in the use of prayer and the selection of scripture is to keep the individual close to reality. There is a natural tendency to withdraw from pain. Neither scripture nor prayer should be used in such a way as to imply escapism or a fitting of the teachings of immortality over the top of the pain prematurely. For example, the twenty-third Psalm faces realistically "the valley of the shadow of death," and at the same time emphasizes God's nearness.

Prayer used in the acute phase of bereavement should be brief but should gather up the family's feelings and in its wording recognize the course of normal grief reaction. Beginning with the reality of the loss and the pain of separation the prayer should move on to confess the need for divine strength and courage through the experience.

6. The minister who is present with the family at the hospital during the time of death can frequently alleviate any feelings of impropriety the family might have regarding an autopsy. It is unfortunate that the doctor must request permission for the autopsy during the acute stages of grief, but there is no way this can be avoided. Not only is the doctor confronted by an inappropriate time, but also by popular ignorance of what an autopsy involves. Families may fear disfigurement of the body or resist what seems to them to be an affront to the person's dignity. Some of them think of it as "experimenting" on the body. In one case the family thought the doctor meant the body would then require cremation. The chaplain learned of the family's confusion, and after an explanation they gave their consent.

The family expects the doctor to ask for an autopsy which is why the minister can often succeed in leading them to give permission where the doctor has failed. The desire of the family to know the cause of death can serve as the basis for beginning a conversation directed toward getting permission for post-mortem examination. It should be stressed also that this examination affords the best way known by medicine to extend its frontiers of knowledge which will ultimately help all people.

However, no matter how strongly one might feel about the value of an autopsy, a family should be supported in the fact that the decision is solely theirs, and they should be satisfied with the decision either way, because they will have to live with it.

It is the belief of the authors that unresolved grief is complicating the emotional lives of far more people than most ministers realize. There were danger signals occurring in one out of every ten families in the study presented in this chapter. This means that as the pastor ministers to persons in the acute stages of grief he should be alert to any unhealthy reactions that might complicate later grief work. This study points up the need for further research by the minister himself as to how his role and the resources of the Christian religion can be made more effective in the prevention of morbid grief reactions and the facilitation of healthy grief work.

There is no greater crisis that can come to a family than the loss of one of its loved ones through death. Historically man has always called upon whatever religious beliefs he possessed in the face of this mystery. Despite any effect secularism may have had upon the minister's role in our culture today, he remains the chief figure in our society charged with the responsibility of bringing comfort to the bereaved.

For Further Reading

DEUTSCH, HELENE. "Absence of Grief," *Psychoanalytic Quarterly,* 6:12, 1937.

FREUD, SIGMUND. "Mourning and Melancholia," *Collected Papers.* London: Hogarth Press and the Institute of Psychoanalysis, 1949. Vol. IV:152-70.

IRION, PAUL T. *The Funeral and the Mourners.* Nashville: Abingdon Press, 1954. Pp. 23-61.

JACKSON, EDGAR N. *Understanding Grief.* Nashville: Abingdon Press, 1957.

LIEBMAN, JOSHUA LOTH. *Peace of Mind.* New York: Simon and Schuster, 1946. Pp. 105-33.

LINDEMANN, ERICH. "Symptomatology and Management of Acute Grief." *American Journal of Psychiatry,* 101:141-48, Sept. 1944.

ROGERS, WILLIAM F. *Ye Shall Be Comforted.* Philadelphia: Westminster Press, 1950.

WORCESTER, ALFRED. *The Care of the Aged, the Dying and the Dead.* Springfield, Ill.: Charles C. Thomas, 1940.

YOUNG, RICHARD K. *The Pastor's Hospital Ministry.* Nashville: Broadman Press, 1954. Pp. 111-23.

TWELVE *The General Hospital As a Setting for Spiritual Therapy*

Since World War II much has been written about doctor-minister co-operation. During a recent year, for example, over seventy-five articles on religion appeared in medical journals in the United States. In addition, frequent "summit conferences" have been held between leaders in religion and medicine discussing theoretically the values that would accrue from the "healing team approach." Discussion between doctors and ministers is valuable, but the theory of co-operation must move from the conference table to a face-to-face relationship between the doctor and the minister across the bed of the patient.

The complexity of our society and the expanding scope of human knowledge have compelled a high degree of specialization within the professions. Specialization has made possible better patient care and lengthened the span of life; at the same time it has resulted in too many instances in a partial and fragmentary approach to the patient as a person. More and more both professions are realizing that a comprehensive approach to healing can be accomplished only when each admits he does not have all the answers.

The unconscious tendency to play God is an occupational hazard in both the ministry and medicine. This is probably due to the

The authors wish to acknowledge their gratitude to Reid T. Holmes, Fellow, American College of Hospital Administrators and Administrator, North Carolina Baptist Hospital, for a critical reading of this chapter.

fact that members of both professions are constantly dealing in ultimates. For instance, when several physicians agree upon a diagnosis, it is an ex-cathedra communication to the mind of the layman and is not subject to debate. Likewise, the minister deals with ultimates as he stands in the pulpit and proclaims the eternal truths of the Bible. The clergyman's habit of speaking of "my parishioner" and the physician's habit of saying "my patient" can unconsciously connote a possessiveness which is detrimental to the healing team approach.

There is no sharp line of demarcation between body, mind, and spirit. In fact, neither exists as an entity except in relation to the others. For this reason there can be no mechanically simple definitions of function between the doctor and the minister. There must necessarily be overlapping when each is using the same set of facts in personality background. Thus, the common meeting ground of the doctor and the minister is in the middle of the emotional and spiritual life of the individual. This demands a greater degree of maturity than when each is working separately in his own little sphere. When the welfare of the patient is the first concern, the team members are not disturbed by the overlapping in their ministry and thereby a therapeutic community is created.

The ideal which we have been describing has been set forth in poetic form by Kelley Barnett: "Across the patient's bed we face each other; you in your white coat, a stethoscope in your hand; I in my black coat with a prayerbook in my hand. At the beginning we were one, since the beginning we have always been together, unavoidably related, and when you are true to the oath of medicine and I true to the ordination vows, the center of interest has been, is and must always be in the man on the bed, your patient, my parishioner, God's creation. And if we work in unity together, the patient will come to see, to know, to love the Father God who through us, in us, by us, and in *spite* of us, remains, the Ultimate One Who '. . . healeth all our diseases and forgiveth all our iniquities.'"[1]

The Church in recognition of the hospital as a setting for pastoral care has provided in recent years full-time chaplains to work with physicians in larger municipal and denominational hospitals.

Hardly anything, however, has been done to give structure to doctor-minister co-operation at the grass-roots level in small community hospitals. There are thousands of fifty and seventy-five bed hospitals in rural and urban communities in the United States where ministers and doctors oftentimes serve the same individual without ever communicating with one another. In most communities there is a county medical society and an interdenominational ministers' conference. But in the history of the typical community the organizations have never had a joint meeting to discuss the practical problems that each experiences in trying to relate with and supplement the other profession in their own community hospital.

The Department of Pastoral Care of the North Carolina Baptist Hospital has formulated a plan for a volunteer chaplaincy program as a means of fostering closer teamwork between doctors and ministers. A volunteer chaplaincy is an arrangement whereby the interdenominational ministers' conference sets up for the community hospital a duty roster of local ministers each of whom serves as acting chaplain for a week. The primary duties of the volunteer chaplain are to visit patients who have no church affiliation and to take emergency calls, day or night.

After having met the doctors and ministers at a joint meeting in twenty-five different communities and seeing the enthusiastic response to a volunteer chaplaincy plan for their hospital we are convinced that it constitutes an excellent medium for co-operation at the grass-roots level. Pastors who have participated in such a program report certain specific practical benefits:

1. A vital missionary opportunity is found in the local hospital. Currently about twenty million people in our nation spend some time in a general hospital each year. This means that about one in every eight persons in our society is hospitalized each year which makes the hospital almost a crossroads for humanity. The hospital environment is certainly no place for high-powered, highly emotional evangelism. However, nearly fourteen years of experience in our hospital have convinced us that there is no institution or place in our society that affords a greater opportunity to bring the message of Christ to bear upon human need than a general hospital.

2. The teaching of "comprehensive medicine" in medical schools today is tending to create a demand for the minister as a member of the healing team. Every minister should have a close working relationship with the physicians in his community and what better place to meet them and get acquainted than in the local hospital where both are already at work.

3. Fly-by-night evangelists who are constantly getting into the hospitals create a bad impression which reflects eventually on all ministers. The organized effort in their local hospitals by pastors who are seeking to improve their ministry to the physically ill will break down many barriers that have been and still are existing between the medical profession and the minister. This will solve problems for the other professional people in the hospital since they can say, in no uncertain terms, to the minister who is going from room to room that he must confine his visits to the members of his own church as the hospital already has an organized pastoral ministry.

The first question usually raised by the busy pastor is, "How in the world can I find time to serve two or three weeks out of the year as a chaplain in the hospital with all the work I already have to do?" Some of these same busy men are now saying the personal satisfaction gained from this intense experience was more than adequate compensation for the time involved. These pastors have found that the program is readily accepted by the entire community and that they themselves become engaged in a deeper relationship with other professions dedicated to serving those in need. One minister reports more calls from doctors for consulation with their patients during the six months following a joint dinner meeting of local ministers and doctors than he had received in the previous seven years.

The pastor's first step in promoting a volunteer chaplaincy program in a local hospital is to create an interest in the plan at his interdenominational ministers' conference. The following suggestions are offered for the initiation of such a project.

1. The interdenominational ministers' conference should elect a planning committee to set up the volunteer chaplaincy program. This committee should meet with the local hospital administrator

and the director of the nursing service or invite these two people to an open meeting of the ministers' conference to discuss how the pastor can make his hospital ministry more effective. It is essential to secure the co-operation of the hospital administrator and the director of the nursing service since they are well aware of any peculiar circumstances that might exist in the local hospital situation.

2. The planning committee should then arrange a dinner meeting for the interdenominational ministers' conference and the medical society. Each minister may personally invite as his guest one physician or if doctors take the initiative they can each invite a minister. In this way, a better attendance is assured and the minister and the physician become better acquainted. A speaker should be engaged for the meeting to speak on a subject of mutual interest, such as "The Common Meeting Ground between the Doctor and the Minister."

3. The next step is to arrange a workshop or clinic for the pastors who will participate in the volunteer chaplaincy service. This workshop might include such subjects as hospital etiquette, handling crisis situations, the use of religious resources, and how to make referrals. Our experience suggests the advisability of using in the volunteer chaplaincy program only those ministers who take part in the workshop. Some communities are having a workshop annually as a refresher for those co-operating in the program and for new ministers who move into the area.

4. A schedule is prepared containing the names of the pastors who will serve as a chaplain to the hospital each week. All pastors who participate serve at least one week at a time. The plan where the pastor has served as chaplain for one day at a time does not work. A patient's average stay in the general hospital is approximately seven days. The pastor who serves for a full week is able to build sustained relationships with patients.

5. The chairman of the planning committee ordinarily becomes the chaplain supervisor. He should post with the telephone operator at the hospital the name of the minister who will be chaplain for the week. The operator should also have the home telephone numbers of the chaplain and the chaplain supervisor. This means that the chap-

lain supervisor is called if the pastor on call for that week cannot be reached. The chaplain of the week should keep the telephone operator at the hospital informed of his whereabouts whenever he leaves the institution.

6. Ministers who participate in the volunteer chaplaincy program should explain the program to their congregations. This will make it possible for them to be relatively unencumbered by their own church responsibilities during the week they are on duty. We have yet to learn of a church that did not co-operate fully with its pastor. If an emergency makes it impossible for a man to serve, he should exchange weeks with another minister and notify the hospital of the change.

7. The volunteer chaplain should keep an accurate record of his visitation. One ministerial association keeps a book of record forms which are made in duplicate. The chaplain supervisor keeps a carbon copy which is used to compile a yearly report made to the hospital administrator and the ministerial association. A record form might include the following information: Number of new admissions; Number of admissions referred to their own minister; Number of visits to patients, and per patient; Number of contacts with families; Number of referrals from nurses; Number of referrals from doctors; Number of religious commitments.

8. The pastor chaplain begins his day at the hospital by checking the list of new admissions. Usually the hospital admission records list the patient's religious denomination. It should be made clear that the pastor chaplain is not in the hospital to visit patients who have an active church affiliation except those of his own congregation. He is there to visit patients who would otherwise have no religious ministry and to take emergency calls, day or night.

Regardless of whether or not there is a structured volunteer chaplaincy service in his local hospital, the minister still needs to work in close collaboration with the physician who is treating his parishioners. First of all, the minister should be familiar with the well-established rules which ought to be observed in hospital visitation. Obviously this entire book presupposes a knowledge of these basic fundamentals. Boisterous conversation, loud praying, lumbering into the room without being announced, long visits when the patient is tired, and aggressively forcing religion upon the patient are errors of etiquette that will hinder the establishment of a meaningful relationship.[2]

In the second place, the minister will need to be aware of the distinctions between more formal types of pastoral counseling and the bedside ministry. Thus far, students in clinical training programs and pastors have had to draw upon the literature of pastoral counseling and make their own application of these principles to counseling with the sick.

Pastoral care of the sick embraces counseling, but the goal in the care of the sick is not necessarily to attempt to structure a counseling relationship with every patient. Too often in clinical training the student is tempted to gauge his success solely by the "depth" of his relationship without regard to the patient's actual need. The situation may well call for humor, social conversation, and encouragement which at the time can be strategic forms of ministry. Attention should always focus on the patient's need at the moment rather than upon a case-history approach.

We recognize that counseling is counseling anytime an individual is sharing his life with someone who he feels can help him understand his problem, whether it takes place on a street corner, in an office, or in a sickroom. Nevertheless, the setting does exert a shaping influence upon the process, and nowhere is this more obvious than in a hospital room.

The problem of moving from office counseling to a bedside ministry has been called to our attention intensively during the past years. In a program of clinical pastoral education we attempt to teach both office counseling and the pastoral care of the sick simultaneously to chaplain-interns on one-year internships. These men visit hospital patients in the morning, and see out-patient counselees in the afternoon. It is therefore essential that they learn how the setting influences the application of counseling principles. The pastor likewise faces the problem of moving from counseling with parishioners in his study to the pastoral care of the sick in the hospital.

The translation of the principles of office counseling for use in bedside ministry is affected by certain environmental factors. In the care of the sick one will still use his knowledge of personality development, skill in listening, warmth of acceptance, and various other counseling skills. The principles are similar, but there are sufficient differences between office counseling and the bedside ministry significantly to influence the manner in which each ministry is performed.

1. Within the hospital setting, the minister must necessarily work alongside other professional people whereas in the setting of the pastor's study he may be the only person attempting to help the individual. The parishioner goes to the hospital to receive medical care, and any contribution the pastor can make must necessarily be correlated with the overall medical goal. Teamwork requires that the members trust each other and have some degree of understanding of each other's function. Where there is no working relationship, ministers have become hostile over a simple thing like a "no visitors" sign, not realizing that the patient's life might be hanging in the balance to the point that any emotional upset could affect the outcome. In similar fashion, doctors have misunderstood a patient's anxiety which occasionally follows a minister's visit. That is, in the minister's work an individual sometimes "has to get worse before getting better." Guilt reaction precipitated by a visit from the minister may create anxiety which is alleviated when the patient decides to face up to what is causing his guilt and do something about it. Thus, the bedside ministry requires a greater sensitivity to interprofessional relationships. It is necessary that the minister and doctor keep in communication and grow together in their understanding of the patient and his progress.

2. There may be unavoidable interruptions during a hospital visit whereas the minister is more in control of the situation in his own study. Very few people who have not worked over an extended period of time in a hospital environment realize the intricate, complex problem of caring for several hundred sick people. Meals, housecleaning, bedmaking, medications, laboratory work, temperature and blood pressure checks, doctors' visits, and nursing care must all go according to schedule. There will be fewer interruptions if

the nurse has announced the pastor or knows he is making a call.

3. Counseling in a general hospital setting tends to be of short duration whereas the pastor sets his own limitation on the number of times he will see an individual in his study. The brevity of the patient's stay in a general hospital limits the number of interviews with the individual. Unlike the hospital chaplain, the pastor has a distinct advantage in that he can see the person before, during, and after his hospitalization.

4. The pastor takes the initiative in his ministry to the sick whereas the counselee takes the initiative when he requests an office appointment. The relationship to a person consciously seeking help for a specific problem is far different from the relationship to an individual in a crisis who has not called for help. In fact the patient may be paying twenty dollars a day for a private room and any person visiting him should observe the same courtesies that would apply to calls made in his home. Hence, direct questions are more appropriate in the office or study than in the hospital room. Although the emotions do vitally affect one's health, the pastor should never assume that illness is prima-facie evidence of an emotional problem. A question sometimes asked the teacher of pastoral care is, "Do you approach every person as though he has a problem?" Certainly the minister does not approach every patient as though his emotions were a primary factor in his illness. Every person, however, has normal concerns in life, and in a friendly relationship will express these concerns.

5. The hospitalized patient is sick and often in pain, whereas the counselee who comes to the office may be in excellent physical health. The illness may intensify the person's need to talk, but at the same time the elements of weakness and discomfort can be distracting influences during an interview. For this reason hospital visits may vary from one to forty minutes in length in contrast to office interviews which are almost uniformly fifty to sixty minutes. Except in unusual circumstances counseling sessions at the bedside should be restricted to thirty to forty minutes in length, regardless of how well the patient may appear.

6. Members of the patient's family are often encountered in

the hospital whereas they may or may not be known to the pastor in a formal interview. Having access to members of the family is at times a help but at other times can be a hindrance. There are occasions when a relative will attempt to badger the pastor into getting the patient to make a religious commitment. Or, in other instances, a relative may say to the pastor, "While he's in the hospital I wish you would talk to Jim about his drinking." A good response for the minister when caught in this dilemma is, "Well, of course, he is not aware that I know anything about his drinking. Do you mind if I tell him you have talked with me about this?" Invariably, the person who makes this sort of a request replies, "No, no, don't tell him that," to which the pastor may say, "You will realize, then, that I am at a disadvantage since I will have no opportunity to help him unless he himself wants to talk with me about it."

The hospital setting affords the pastor an opportunity to gain further insight into the patient's personality by observing the interactions of the family. Illness often reveals the true elements of beauty as well as of ugliness in human relationships neither of which is evident in more normal times. Thus, the sickroom becomes a stage, and the pastor the audience for the enactment of the dramas of husband-wife, parent-child, and brother-sister relationships. The crisis of illness can bring to the surface love, courage, and loyalty as well as overprotection, immaturity, sibling rivalry, and in some cases outright conflict. The wise pastor will be alert to all these clues for a deeper understanding of the patient and his needs.

7. Confessions made to the pastor during hospital visits are often precipitated by the duress of fear, pain, and the pressures of illness, whereas those made in office counseling are more likely to be the result of planning and deliberation. A premature confession can be made before the person has established a secure interpersonal relationship to his pastor. Therefore it is always well to thank an individual after a confession for having enough confidence to share his intimate experiences. Unless this reassurance is given, the person may regret having talked, which accounts for a coolness sometimes encountered on the next visit.

There are few times in life when we let another person inside "the castles of our souls." Whenever a minister is allowed to "walk around" on the inside of another person's life he should "take off his hat and pull off his shoes" and realize that he is on holy ground. If there is any such thing as holy ground in this universe, it is in the middle of an individual human soul, and not under an apple tree somewhere. For this reason information divulged in a confessional relationship must be respected as privileged communication. If this information seems pertinent to the patient's illness ask his permission to share the facts with the physician or encourage the patient to do so himself.

Bearing in mind the environmental differences between the pastor's study and the hospital room, basic counseling principles can be employed in the bedside ministry. These principles need no elaboration here. It is in order, however, to mention several cautions which should be observed when counseling in the sickroom. The pastor may know his parishioner casually, but may not have had a previous opportunity to deal with him intimately. Therefore it is important to bear in mind that in all counseling the relationship between the counselor and the counselee is of primary importance. The use of any counseling principle depends upon the strength of this relationship and sometimes upon the strength of the sick patient!

In contrast to office counseling, it is not appropriate to expect a sick person to carry the burden of the conversation. However important it is to be a good listener, the use of the listening principle when standing by a sickbed looking down at a patient should be carefully guarded. Silences, which may be appropriate to the office situation, have no place in the hospital ministry unless an unusually good relationship has been established with the patient. It is not unusual for a mature and poised patient to interpret ill-timed listening as inadequacy on the part of the minister. This is occasionally observed in the first few interviews written by a theological student in clinical training. Following his visit the patient may remark to a a roommate, "I felt sorry for that young minister. He seemed so timid." Yet the student went away thinking he had done a good job of listening.

A further caution should be made with reference to the use in bedside counseling of various techniques to keep the individual talking without diverting the course of the conversation. Such phrases as "I see," "Uh-huh," "Is that right?" and reflecting the patient's last sentence, are sometimes employed for this purpose. Counseling with the sick person calls for more contribution by the counselor to the conversation and more care in using this technique than is required in office counseling. In both office and hospital, of course, one should always guard against unconsciously falling into the habit of repeatedly using one of these phrases, such as "Uh-huh," or simply reflecting the patient's statements. The overuse of any one of these phrases can be absurd.

In counseling with the sick it is wise not to explore areas of the patient's life which he has not brought up for discussion. Of course questions that are acceptable in any social situation can be used, but to pry into the patient's illness or personality background is not in keeping with the minister's role in the sickroom. When the patient has introduced a subject voluntarily, the minister is at liberty to discuss the subject and even to ask questions about it.

The medical profession today is more receptive to the place of religion in the healing ministry than at any time since the priest and the physician were one and the same person. The partnership between doctors and ministers has been found effective and its value demonstrated through the work of chaplains in a limited number of large hospitals in this country.

Now the time has come for this partnership to be realized throughout our society. Too often the sick person is dealt with by the physician and the minister without the knowledge of their common effort and goal and in some instances all three individuals are members of the same church. The pathetic weakness lies in the fact that each worker, too often, is going his own way, whether he carries a black bag or a Bible, with little attempt at communication with the other. In our experience in a medical center we have been impressed with the frequency with which people have been referred to us from the local community whose illnesses responded to treatment only when the minister and the doctor worked together in a unified team approach. There is no excuse for professional leaders in a community to allow their personal immaturities to perpetuate a form of "therapeutic imperialism" at the expense of the patient. The healing of these people is both the justification and the reward for collaborative efforts. To see a person having been shackled and bound mentally, physically, and spiritually being emancipated by the blended efforts of a healing team and to have a part in this venture is worth all the discipline it demands.

The attempt in this book to demonstrate the pastoral care of the hospitalized patient has made us extremely conscious of the need for further research. Much of our present progress in medical science is based heavily upon the keeping of accurate records in the treatment of disease. If the pastor in working with his local physician could come to realize the importance of keeping accurate records of his pastoral care of the sick, the healing ministry of the church could conceivably be revolutionized!

For Further Reading

BIRD, BRIAN. *Talking with Patients*. Philadelphia: J. B. Lippincott Company, 1955.

BURLING, TEMPLE, LENTZ, EDITH, AND WILSON, ROBERT. *The Give and Take in Hospitals*. New York: G. P. Putnam's Sons, 1956.

CABOT, RICHARD C., AND DICKS, RUSSELL L. *The Art of Ministering to the Sick*. New York: The Macmillan Company, 1947.

IKIN, A. GRAHAM. *New Concepts of Healing*. New York: Association Press, 1956.

SOUTHARD, SAMUEL. *Religion and Nursing*. Nashville: Broadman Press, 1959.

"Special Issue on The Ministry to the Sick," *Pastoral Psychology*, 8:73, April 1957.

WESTBERG, GRANGER. *Nurse, Pastor, and Patient*. Rock Island, Ill.: Augustana Press, 1955.

YOUNG, RICHARD K. *The Pastor's Hospital Ministry*. Nashville: Broadman Press, 1954.

YOUNG, RICHARD K., AND PATRICK, BENJAMIN. "Outpatient Pastoral Counseling in a Medical Center," *Journal of the American Medical Association*. 168:24-26, Sept. 6, 1958.

REFERENCES

Chapter One. *Spiritual Therapy for the Heart Patient*

1. Cited by Robert McMillan, M.D.
2. *Ibid.*
3. William N. Chambers, Joseph L. Grant, and Kerr L. White, "The Patient and Physician in Cardiac Symptom Formation," *Journal of the American Medical Association,* 168:1617-22, Nov. 22, 1958.
4. Aubrey R. Johnson, *The Vitality of the Individual in the Thought of Ancient Israel* (Cardiff: University of Wales Press, 1949), p. 77.
5. Chambers, Grant, and White, *op. cit.,* p. 1618.
6. *Ibid.,* p. 1619.

Chapter Two. *Spiritual Therapy for the Peptic Ulcer Patient*

1. David Cayer, M.D., personal communication.
2. W. L. Palmer, "Peptic Ulcer," in Russell L. Cecil and Robert F. Loeb, *A Textbook of Medicine,* 8th ed. (Philadelphia: W. B. Saunders Company, 1915), p. 700.
3. David Cayer, M.D.
4. *Ibid.*
5. Flanders Dunbar, *Mind and Body: Psychosomatic Medicine* (New York: Random House, 1955), pp. 163-64.
6. Stewart Wolf, "Summary of Evidence Relating Life Situation and Emotional Stress to Peptic Ulcer," *Annals of Internal Medicine,* 31:637-49, Oct. 1949.
7. Albert J. Sullivan and Frederick C. Rehfelt, "The Spirit and the Flesh," *Southern Medical Journal,* 43:736-43, Aug. 1950.

175

Chapter Three. *Spiritual Therapy for the Ulcerative Colitis Patient*

1. Edward Weiss and O. Spurgeon English, *Psychosomatic Medicine* (Philadelphia: W. B. Saunders Company, 1957), p. 255.
2. Marcus F. Sohmer, M.D., personal communication.
3. Sullivan and Rehfelt, *loc. cit.*
4. Erich Lindemann, "Life Stress and Bodily Disease," *Research Publications, Association for Research in Nervous and Mental Diseases* (Baltimore: Williams and Wilkins Company, 1950), p. 706.
5. Sullivan and Rehfelt, *op. cit.*, p. 741.
6. J. Groen, "Psychogenesis and Psychotherapy of Ulcerative Colitis," *Psychosomatic Medicine,* 9:151, May-June 1947.
7. Cited by Sullivan and Rehfelt, *loc. cit.*
8. Sullivan and Rehfelt, *op. cit.*, p. 738.
9. Erich Lindemann, "Psychiatric Aspects of the Conservative Treatment of Ulcerative Colitis," *Archives of Neurology and Psychiatry,* 53:322, 1945.
10. Frank C. Bone, Julian M. Ruffin, George J. Baylin, and Chester Cassel, "The Clinical Course of Idiopathic Ulcerative Colitis," *Southern Medical Journal,* 43:817-823, Sept. 1950.

Chapter Four. *Spiritual Therapy for the Asthma Patient*

1. Flanders Dunbar, *op. cit.*, p. 186.
2. Franz Alexander, *Psychosomatic Medicine* (New York: W. W. Norton, 1950), p. 133.
3. Dunbar, *op. cit.*, p. 182.
4. T. M. French, F. Alexander, *et al,* "Psychogenic Factors in Bronchial Asthma," *Psychosomatic Medicine Monographs* (Washington: National Research Council, 1941).
5. T. F. Treuting and H. S. Ripley, "Life Situations, Emotions, and Bronchial Asthma," *Journal of Nervous and Mental Disease,* 108:380-98, Nov. 1948.
6. Peter H. Knapp and S. J. Nemetz, "Personality Variations in Bronchial Asthma," *Psychosomatic Medicine,* 19:443-65, Nov.-Dec. 1957.
7. *Ibid,* p. 462.
8. Peter H. Knapp and S. J. Nemetz, "Sources of Tension in Bronchial Asthma," *Psychosomatic Medicine,* 19:466-85, Nov.-Dec. 1957.
9. Alexander, *op. cit.*, p. 139.

Chapter Five. *Spiritual Therapy for the Skin Patient*

1. Brian Bird, "Certain Observations upon the Relationship of Anger and Eczema," *American Practitioner and Digest of Treatment,* 9:929-32, June 1958.

2. Charles Howell, M.D., personal communication.
3. Stuart Maddin, "How Important Are Psychosomatic Factors in the Field of Dermatology?" *Canadian Medical Association Journal,* 77:555, Sept. 15, 1957.
4. Eric Wittkower and Brian Russell, *Emotional Factors in Skin Disease* (New York: Paul B. Hoeber, Inc., 1953).
5. Quoted by Wittkower and Russell, *op. cit.,* p. 24.
6. Maddin, *loc. cit.*
7. Wittkower and Russell, *op. cit.,* p. 141.
8. Ludwig Köhler, *Hebrew Man* (London: SCM Press, 1956), pp. 56-57.
9. Wittkower and Russell, *op. cit.,* p. 84.
10. Stephen Rush, *et al.,* "Neurodermatitis and Emotional Tension," *A.M.A. Archives of Dermatology,* 76:766, Dec. 1957.

Chapter Six. *Spiritual Therapy for the Migraine Patient*

1. Weiss and English, *op. cit.,* p. 445.
2. Thomas J. Walsh, "An Approach to the Headache Problem," *Journal of the Bowman Gray School of Medicine,* 17:54, June 1959.
3. Martin Netsky, M.D., personal communication.
4. Weiss and English, *op. cit.,* p. 453.
5. John Gardner, George E. Mountain, and Edgar A. Hines, Jr., "The Relationship of Migraine to Hypertension and Hypertension Headache," *The American Journal of the Medical Sciences,* 200:50-53, July 1940.
6. Grace A. Touraine and George Draper, "The Migrainous Patient," *Journal of Nervous and Mental Disease,* 80:1-15, July 1934.
7. Robert M. Marcussen and Harold G. Wolff, "A Formulation of the Dynamics of the Migraine Attack," *Psychosomatic Medicine,* 11:251-56, Sept.-Oct. 1949.
8. W. D. Ross and F. L. McNaughton, "Objective Personality Studies in Migraine by Means of the Rorschach Method," *Psychosomatic Medicine,* 7:73-79, March 1945.
9. Cited by Weiss and English, *op. cit.,* p. 456.
10. Marcussen and Wolff, *loc. cit.*
11. *Ibid.*

Chapter Seven. *Spiritual Therapy for the Patient with Anxiety and Conversion Reaction*

1. Edward Weiss and O. Spurgeon English, *Psychosomatic Medicine* (Philadelphia: W. B. Saunders Company, 1943), p. 1.
2. O. Spurgeon English and Stuart M. Finch, *Introduction to Psychiatry* (New York: W. W. Norton & Company, 1954), p. 158.
3. *Ibid.,* p. 159.

4. *Ibid.,* p. 164.

5. *Ibid.,* p. 165.

6. John L. Lightburn, Richard B. Cattell, and William F. Stevenson, "Differential Diagnosis of Conversion Reaction in a General Hospital," *Postgraduate Medicine,* 23:140-47, Feb. 1958.

7. English and Finch, *op. cit.,* p. 164.

8. William Brown and Joseph Pisetsky, "Sociopsychologic Factors in Hysterical Paraplegia," *Journal of Nervous and Mental Disease,* 119:294, April 1954.

9. Harry A. Wilmer and Richard E. Scammon, "Neuropsychiatric Patients Reported Cured at St. Bartholomew's Hospital in the Twelfth Century," *Journal of Nervous and Mental Disease,* 119:11, Jan. 1954.

10. Brian Bird, *Talking with Patients* (Philadelphia: J. B. Lippincott, 1955), p. 27.

Chapter Eight.   *Spiritual Therapy for the Surgical Patient*

1. Bernard C. Meyer, "Some Psychiatric Aspects of Surgical Practice," *Psychosomatic Medicine,* 20:206, May-June 1958.

2. Melvin I. Gibbel, "Pitfalls in Preoperative and Postoperative Care," *Surgical Clinics of North America,* 38:43, Feb. 1958.

3. Karl A. Menninger, "Polysurgery and Polysurgical Addiction," *Psychoanalytic Quarterly,* 3:173, 1934.

4. Cited by Norman Chivers and Theodore L. Dorpat, "Emotional Reactions to Surgical Procedures," *GP* 17:108-11, May 1958.

5. Ibid. See also Edward S. Tauber, "Effects of Castration upon the Sexuality of the Adult Male," *Psychosomatic Medicine,* 2:74-87, Jan. 1940.

6. Howard Bradshaw, M.D., personal communication.

7. Meyer, *op. cit.,* pp. 209-10.

8. Douglas Noble, Douglas B. Price, and Rodman Gilder, "Psychiatric Disturbances Following Amputation," *American Journal of Psychiatry,* 110:609, Feb. 1954.

9. Meyer, *op. cit.,* p. 207.

10. R. L. Kelham, "Some Thoughts on Mental Effects of Amputation," *British Medical Journal,* 1:334, Feb. 8, 1958.

11. Julius Huffman, "Phantom Limb Syndrome," *The Journal of Nervous and Mental Disease,* 119:261-70, March 1954.

12. H. H. Kessler, "Psychological Preparation of the Amputee," *Industrial Medicine and Surgery,* 20:107-8, March 1951.

13. Gibbel, *op. cit.,* p. 42.

14. Meyer, *op. cit.,* p. 213.

15. Thomas J. Canty, "Amputation Stump Pain," *U.S. Armed Forces Medical Journal,* 9:635, May 1958.

16. Milton O. Lowenthal, Abraham O. Posniak, and Jerome S. Tobis, "Rehabilitation of the Elderly Double Above-Knee Amputee," *Archives of Physical Medicine and Rehabilitation,* 39:290-295, May, 1958.

Chapter Nine. *Spiritual Therapy at the Birth of Children*

1. Frank Lock, M.D., personal communication.
2. Park J. White, "Helping Parents of Congenitally Malformed Children," *Religion & Health*, 1:24, Sept. 1952.
3. According to C. Nash Herndon, M.D., Professor of Medical Genetics, Bowman Gray School of Medicine.
4. Park J. White, *op. cit.*, p. 23.
5. *Statistical Abstract of the United States*, 1959 (Washington, D. C.: U.S. Bureau of Census), p. 56.
6. Leontine Young, *Out of Wedlock* (New York: McGraw-Hill Book Company, 1954).

Chapter Ten. *Spiritual Therapy during the Involutional Period*

1. Weiss and English, *op. cit.*, p. 255.
2. Wingate M. Johnson, M.D., personal communication.
3. Marion Hilliard, M.D., *A Woman Doctor Looks at Love and Life* (Garden City, N. Y.: Doubleday and Company, 1957), p. 153.
4. Helene Deutsch, *The Psychology of Women.* (New York: Grune & Stratton, 1954) II:459.
5. *Ibid.*
6. O. Spurgeon English and Gerald H. J. Pearson, *Emotional Problems of Living* (London: George Allen and Unwin, 1947), p. 391.
7. Editorial, "Is There a True Male Climacteric?" *Journal of the American Medical Association*, 155:1427, Aug. 14, 1954.
8. Dr. Wingate Johnson, who has had long experience with patients in the involutional period, feels that sentiment often leads husband and wife to sleep in the same bed when both would rest better in separate beds or even in separate rooms.

Chapter Eleven. *Spiritual Therapy for the Acutely Bereaved*

1. Helene Deutsch, "Absence of Grief," *Psychoanalytic Quarterly*, 6: 12, 1937.
2. Erich Lindemann, "Symptomatology and Management of Acute Grief," *American Journal of Psychiatry*, 101:141-48, Sept. 1944.
3. Sigmund Freud, "Mourning and Melancholia," *Collected Papers* (London: Hogarth Press and the Institute of Psychoanalysis, 1949), Vol. IV: 152-70.
4. William F. Rogers, *Ye Shall Be Comforted* (Philadelphia: Westminster Press, 1950).
5. Paul T. Irion, *The Funeral and the Mourners* (Nashville: Abingdon Press, 1954).

6. Edgar N. Jackson, *Understanding Grief* (Nashville: Abingdon Press, 1957).

7. The original statistical analysis of these clinical notes was made by Rev. Herbert G. Zerof, Chaplain-intern at North Carolina Baptist Hospital, in preparation for a Th.M. thesis at Southeastern Baptist Theological Seminary.

8. Richard C. Proctor, M.D., personal communication.

9. Deutsch, *op. cit.*

Chapter Twelve. *The General Hospital As a Setting for Spiritual Therapy*

1. Das Kelley Barnett, "Religion and Medicine—Allies or Adversaries," *GP,* 14:75, Sept. 1956.

2. See Richard K. Young, *The Pastor's Hospital Ministry* (Nashville: Broadman Press, 1954), pp. 52-73., and also Richard C. Cabot and Russell L. Dicks, *The Art of Ministering to the Sick* (New York: The Macmillan Company, 1936), pp. 20-29.

INDEX